Pearson Edexcel GCSE (9–1) History

Crime and punishment in Britain, c1000–present

Simon Davis

Published by Pearson Education Limited, 80 Strand, London, WC2R ORL.

www.pearsonschoolsandfecolleges.co.uk

Copies of official specifications for all Pearson qualifications may be found on the website: qualifications.pearson.com

Typeset and illustrated by Newgen KnowledgeWorks Pvt. Ltd. Chennai, India
Produced by Out of House Publishing

First published 2018

21 20 19 18
10 9 8 7 6 5 4 3 2 1

British Library Cataloguing in Publication Data
A catalogue record for this book is available from the British Library

ISBN 978 1 292 24525 6

Printed in Slovakia by Neografia

Acknowledgements
The authors and publisher would like to thank the following individuals and organisations for their kind permission to reproduce copyright material.

Text Credit(s)
11, 15 Duckworth: Annual Report on the Sanitary Condition of the Whitechapel District (with vital statistics) for the year 1889, pp. 20–1 in East End 1888: A year in a London borough among the labouring poor / W.J. Fishman / 1988 **20 Duckworth:** East End 1888: A year in a London borough among the labouring poor / W.J. Fishman / 1988 **21 Routledge:** M. Laing Meason, "Detective Police", The Nineteenth Century 13, 1883, pp. 756–7 in Crime and Punishment in England: A sourcebook / Andrew Barrett and Christopher Harrison / 1999.

Photographs
(key: b-bottom; c-centre; l-left; r-right; t-top)

Alamy stock photo: Lebrecht/Bridgeman Images 11, Historical Images Archive 21, 25. **Mary Evans:** Peter Higginbotham 20.

Printed in Slovakia by Neografia

Notes from the publisher

1. While the publishers have made every attempt to ensure that advice on the qualifications and its assessment is accurate, the official specification and associated guidance materials are the only authoritative source of information and should always be referred to for definitive guidance. Pearson examiners have not contributed to any sections in this resource relevant to examination papers for which they have responsibility.

2. Pearson has robust editorial processes, including answer and fact checks, to ensure the accuracy of the content in this publication, and every effort is made to ensure this publication is free of errors. We are, however, only human, and occasionally errors do occur. Pearson is not liable for any misunderstandings that arise as a result of errors in this publication, but it is our priority to ensure that the content is accurate. If you spot an error, please do contact us at resourcescorrections@pearson.com so we can make sure it is corrected.

Contents

1 Selecting key features

This unit will help you to write short, high-mark descriptions. The skills you will build are how to:

- identify different features related to a topic focus
- select relevant supporting detail
- keep your answer focused and concise.

In the exam, you will be asked to describe features of the past in question 1. This unit will prepare you to write a short descriptive response to questions like the one below.

Exam-style question

Describe **two** features of the problems facing police in Whitechapel.

Feature 1

....

....

Feature 2

....

....

(4 marks)

The three key questions in the **skills boosts** will help you to approach a question focused on description with confidence.

1. How do I identify a key feature?
2. How do I select supporting detail?
3. How do I ensure I do not include too much supporting detail?

Get started

This unit will help you to identify features and find supporting detail, and will offer advice on how to avoid unnecessary explanation.

1. Cross out (~~cat~~) the element that is not needed in an answer for a description question.

   A sentence that identifies a specific feature

   Some information about the feature

   An argument about what the information suggests or proves

2. Supporting information can be a general description of the feature, or a specific example related to it. In the table below, tick (✓) the appropriate column to show whether each of the following details about the problems facing police in Whitechapel provides a feature or specific detail.

	Feature ✓	Specific detail ✓
A Police officers could be attacked.		
B By the 1870s, the Metropolitan Police had to carry out roles defined in 82 laws.		
C In 1888, there were an estimated 62 brothels in Whitechapel.		
D There were a lot of violent drunks in Whitechapel.		
E Police only had a truncheon to protect themselves if attacked.		
F There was a large number of prostitutes on the streets.		

3. In your answer, you only need to state a specific feature in the first sentence and some extra relevant detail in the second. To save time, avoid unnecessary filler sentences or phrases, which do not serve a purpose.

   In each student answer below:

   a Circle (Ⓐ) the specific feature.

   b Underline (A) the relevant detail.

   c Cross out (~~cat~~) any unnecessary filler material.

   The streets of London were dangerous. A detail that demonstrates this is that there were gangs like the Bessarabian Tigers.

   One feature of the problems facing police in Whitechapel is that alcoholism was a serious problem. Whitechapel Road had 45 places that served alcohol on it.

   There was a large number of prostitutes in Whitechapel. From my own knowledge I know that there were 62 brothels in Whitechapel by 1888.

Remember this?

Law enforcement in Whitechapel

This unit uses the theme of law enforcement in Whitechapel to build your skills in selecting key features. If you need to review your knowledge of this theme, work through these pages.

1. a. Cross out ~~cat~~ the four pieces of incorrect information in the paragraph below about policing in Whitechapel.

   b. Now annotate the paragraph with corrections.

Whitechapel was policed by members of H Division, which was a part of the Metropolitan Police Force. H Division had 500 constables out on the beat around Whitechapel. On their beat, constables were not allowed to talk to members of the public unless they were approached by them.

The police faced many difficulties, even though they were popular in poor areas like Whitechapel. They supported public protests and were ordered not to stop them, improving their popularity. However, if they did get into trouble, they only had truncheons to defend themselves.

Policing was a difficult job made worse by the problems of poverty. For example, prostitution was not illegal, but sex workers were vulnerable to attack. Drunks were also a problem, but it was difficult to find places to buy a drink. Finally, gangs ran protection rackets, which the police were powerless to deal with effectively.

2. Facts can be used to support features. What feature could you support with each of the following facts about tensions in Whitechapel? The first has been done for you.

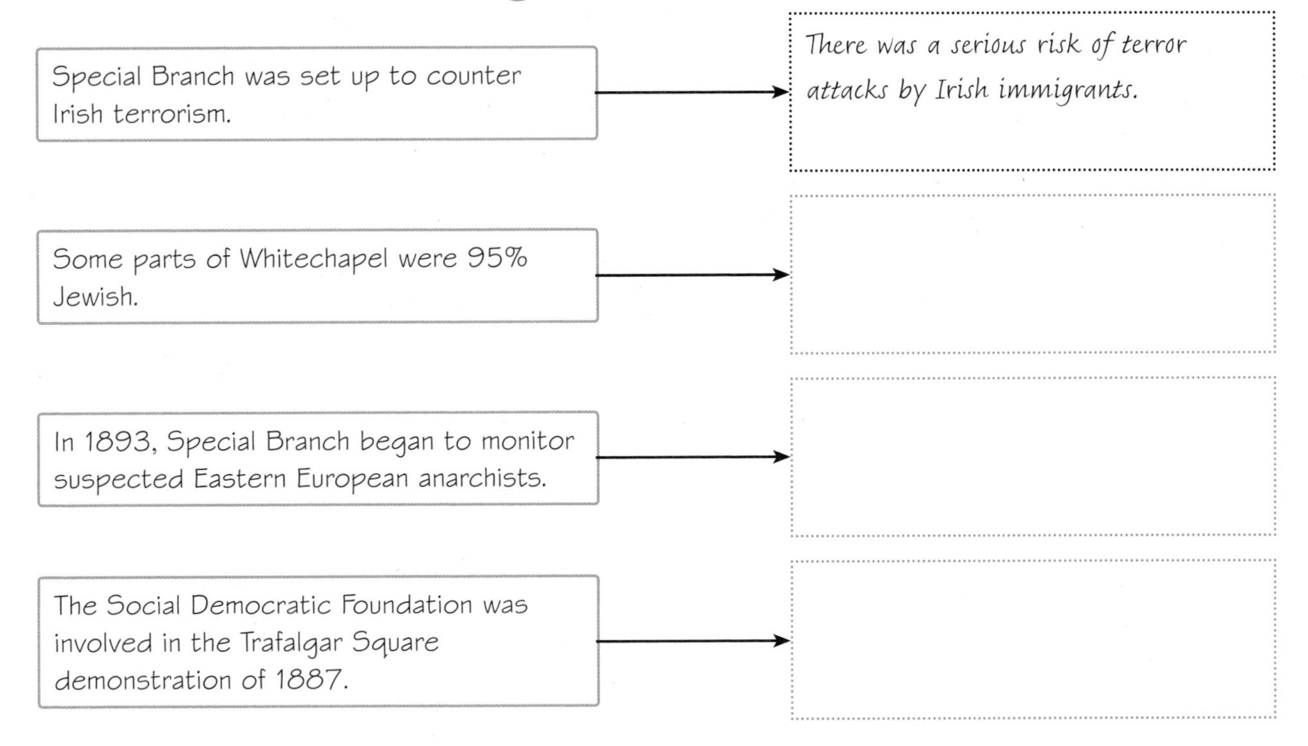

3 Tick ✓ whether the statements below about the conditions in Whitechapel are true or false.

	Statement	true	false
a	In Whitechapel, around 1,000 people out of a population of 30,000 were homeless.	☐	☐
b	Population density was not a problem in Whitechapel.	☐	☐
c	Sweatshop workers could work up to 20 hours a day.	☐	☐
d	Workhouses aimed to give the poor a good standard of living.	☐	☐
e	Unemployment and overcrowding encouraged theft.	☐	☐

4 There were a number of developments in crime and law enforcement in Whitechapel, c1870–c1900. Use your knowledge of these developments to work out which one led to each of the results below. The first has been done for you.

Development		Result
The formation of the Whitechapel Vigilance Committee.	→	The police investigation of Jack the Ripper was damaged.
	→	It was easier to catch repeat criminals.
	→	The accuracy of evidence recording improved.
	→	There was an increase in anti-Semitism.
	→	There was greater fear of anarchist-led terrorism.

How do I identify a key feature?

Question 1 in the exam asks you to 'describe **two** features'. For this, you need to identify two different features related to the topic focus in the question.

Look again at this exam-style question from page 1.

Exam-style question

Describe **two** features of the problems facing police in Whitechapel.

1. Underline Ⓐ the topic focus in the exam-style question.
2. In this part of your course, the topics will all relate to Whitechapel, c1870–c1900: crime, policing and the inner city. Some possible general features for these topics are identified in the left-hand column below. It is important to identify features that are specific. Make them specific by linking ✎ them to the features in the right-hand column.

general feature	specific feature
A Type of people	**a** Overcrowded housing
B The environment	**b** Jewish immigrants
C Use and development of technology	**c** Patrolled the streets
D Policing methods used	**d** Criminal Investigation Department
E Types of crime	**e** Unpopularity of the police
F Ideas and attitudes	**f** Had just begun to use crime-scene photography
G Organisations, groups and departments	**g** Theft of personal property

3. In the table below, change the generic first sentences that identify a feature into specific ones. One student answer is provided to demonstrate the skill. ✎

Generic feature	Specific feature
People created problems for the police.	*Local hostility towards Jewish immigrants caused problems for the police.*
The police dealt with crime.	
The police did not have much technology to make use of.	

How do I select supporting detail?

In order to write a short, supported answer, you need to select detail that is relevant to the feature you have chosen.

Exam-style question

Describe **two** features of the problems facing police in Whitechapel.

① A student's thought process for the selection of supporting detail for the above exam-style question is given below. Complete the blank flow chart.

Identify the feature you are exploring (see Skills Boost 1).
Problems caused by poverty.

↓

Brainstorm what you know about this topic.
- *The residents of Whitechapel lived in overcrowded slums called rookeries, where theft was common.*
- *There were 1,200 prostitutes in Whitechapel in 1888.*
- *Police had to act as unpopular poor-relief officers.*

↓

Choose one piece of detail that either:

elaborates on the feature.	says something specific related to the feature.
The rookeries.	*The number of prostitutes.*

Identify the feature you are exploring (see Skills Boost 1).

↓

Brainstorm what you know about this topic.
-
-
-

↓

Choose one piece of detail that either:

elaborates on the feature.	says something specific related to the feature.

② Look at the first part of one student's answer below. It identifies **one** feature of the problems facing police. Annotate the answer, showing:

a the specific feature it identifies – label it 'feature'

b the detail it uses to support the feature – label it 'detail'.

The police faced problems caused by poverty. The residents of Whitechapel lived in rookeries where theft was common.

③ Now write your two-sentence answer on a separate piece of paper using the ideas you noted in the flow chart in ①.

④ Annotate your response, showing:

a the specific feature it identifies – label it 'feature'

b the detail it uses to support the feature – label it 'detail'.

3 How do I ensure I do not include too much supporting detail?

Your answer to a 'describe **two** features' question should only take five minutes, giving you time to spend on the other questions that are worth more marks. You therefore need to limit the amount of detail you include.

Exam-style question

Describe **two** features of the problems facing police in Whitechapel.

Each feature should meet the following criteria.

State a **specific feature** related to the topic focus.	Include **one** extra sentence for each, elaborating on the feature or providing specific **detail** about it.	**Describe** – do not explain or link features together.

1. Annotate this student answer to the exam-style question above, to show whether the student has followed the criteria above.

One of the problems facing police in Whitechapel was that they were threatened by new working-class political groups. One group was the anarchists, who wanted to overthrow the government. Special Branch decided to set up an operation to monitor suspected anarchists in 1893. Another group was the socialists, who founded the Social Democratic Foundation in 1881. They were involved in the events that led to Bloody Sunday in 1887. Both groups were a problem because they disliked the idea of the police, making the police unpopular, and they were suspected terrorists, so the police had to spend time monitoring them.

2. The answer above, if it were followed by a second feature of similar length, would get full marks. However, it would also take longer than five minutes. Tick two pieces of advice you would give to the student.

Advice	✓
Do not include explanation of the feature.	
Avoid links to other features.	
Do not include more than one piece of additional detail.	
Stop writing after five minutes.	
If you have added something specific, like a date, key term, name or statistic, do not write any more about the feature.	

3. Based on the advice you have chosen, cross out ~~cat~~ the unnecessary material in the student answer above. This should leave you with one specific feature with one supporting detail.

4. Rewrite the student answer on paper. Give the same specific feature but using different supporting information.

You could select from the material you previously crossed out – but remember, you only need one feature and one specific detail.

Sample response

Selecting a key feature and supporting it with the right amount of relevant detail will help you to organise your time in the exam. Analysing another student's answer will provide you with useful practice of this.

Exam-style question

Describe **two** features of the problems facing police in Whitechapel.

Feature 1

They could not make much use of modern technology in their investigations. For example, crime-scene photography was in its very early stages of development. Cameras were used to record some evidence.

Feature 2

Police had to deal with violence between longer-established residents and immigrants. Large numbers of Irish immigrants settled in the East End from the 1840s onwards. They were not well-liked by longer-established residents.

(4 marks)

Key

Feature

Supporting detail

1. The first feature has been annotated. Circle and underline the second feature to annotate it in the same way.

2. There is too much detail in the answer. Cross out two sentences to make the answer more concise. Make sure you do not reduce the number of marks the answer would get. Use the points in the checklist to help you.

Checklist	✓
Do not include an explanation of the feature: your answer should not say what the supporting detail means, proves or suggests.	
Avoid links to other features: your answer does not need to refer to the other feature.	
Do not include more than one piece of additional detail: state a specific feature and give a sentence of supporting information.	
Stop writing after five minutes: your answer should only be a couple of sentences long.	
If you have added something specific, like a date, key term, name or statistic, do not write any more about the feature: this will be enough to make it an effective answer.	

Your turn!

Now it's your turn to try to answer an exam-style question.

Exam-style question

Describe **two** features of the Whitechapel Vigilance Committee.

1. The concept map below suggests general topics you could consider when deciding on features to choose related to the Whitechapel Vigilance Committee. Decide on **two** specific features to explore, by completing **two** of the empty boxes on the diagram. One specific feature has been done for you as an example, but use your own two features in your answer.

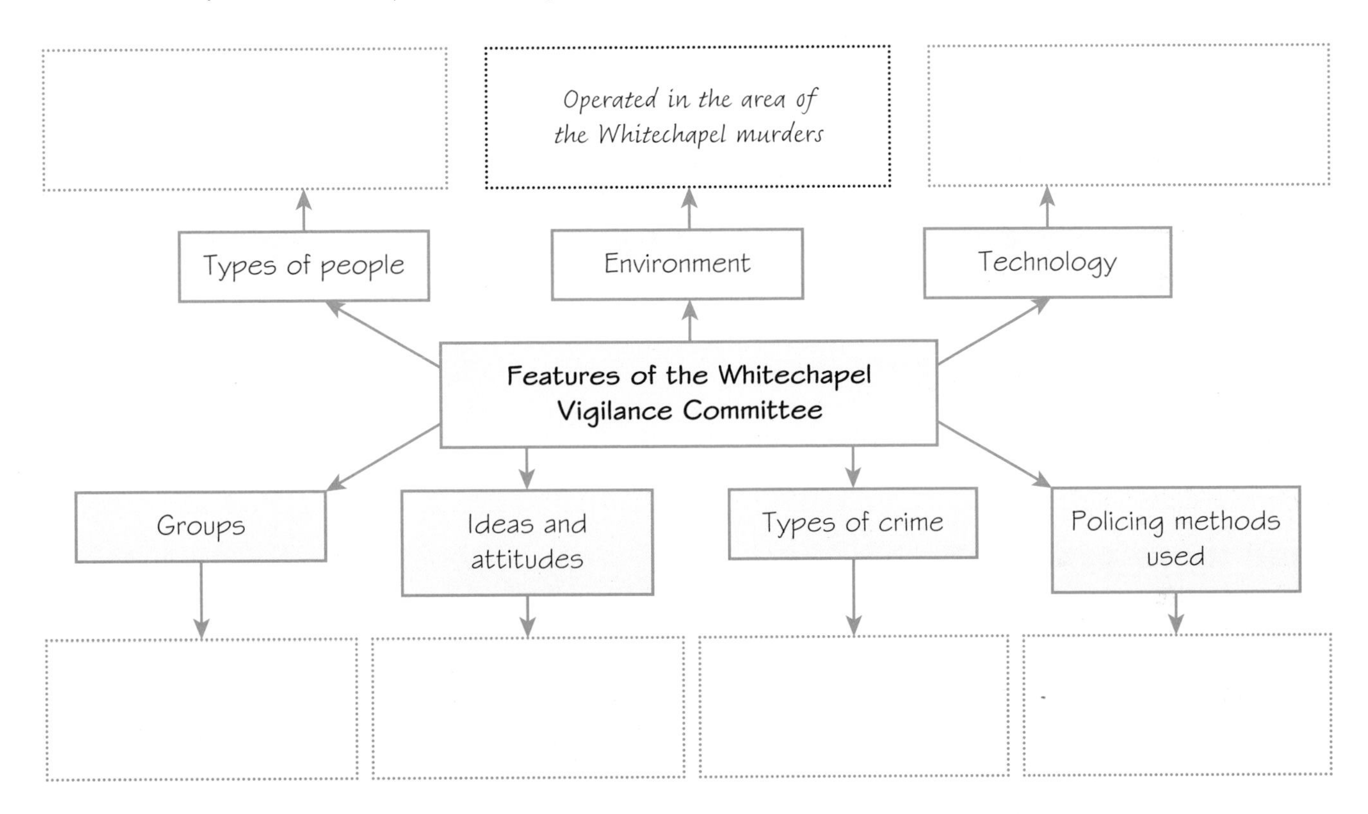

2. Follow the prompts on the writing frame below to write your own answer, now also including a piece of supporting detail for each feature you have chosen.

   a. State your first specific feature: ....

   b. Write a sentence with a supporting detail: ....

   c. State your second specific feature: ....

   d. Write a sentence with a supporting detail: ....

Review your skills

Check up

Review your response to the exam-style question on page 9. Tick the column to show how well you think you have done each of the following.

	Had a go	Nearly there	Got it!
chosen two different specific features related to the question			
selected supporting detail that elaborates on the feature or gives some specific detail			
limited supporting detail to one sentence of relevant material			

Look over all of your work in this unit. Note down three things you have learned that you will apply when answering key features questions.

1 ....

2 ....

3 ....

Need more practice?

On separate paper, try the exam-style question below.

Exam-style question

Describe **two** features of the work of H Division.

Feature 1

....

....

Feature 2

....

....

(4 marks)

How confident do you feel about each of these **skills**? Colour in the bars.

1 How do I identify a key feature?

2 How do I select supporting detail?

3 How do I ensure I do not include too much supporting detail?

Get started

2 Source provenance, usefulness and reliability

This unit will help you to analyse and evaluate the usefulness of a source. The skills you will build are to:

- select criteria for source evaluation
- focus your answer on a specific enquiry
- apply your contextual knowledge to an evaluation of source utility.

In the exam, you will be asked to judge the usefulness of two sources. This unit will prepare you to write your own response to this type of question.

Exam-style question

Study Sources A and B.

How useful are Sources A and B for an enquiry into the the extent of poverty in Whitechapel?

Explain your answer, using Sources A and B and your knowledge of the historical context. **(8 marks)**

Source A *An engraving of Wentworth Street in Whitechapel by Gustav Doré, from a book called* London: A Pilgrimage, *published in 1872. Doré toured London with the journalist who wrote the book and finalised his sketches when he returned to Paris.*

Source B *From a report on sanitary conditions written by Joseph Loane in 1889. Loane was a Medical Officer of Health for the Whitechapel District.*

Rich people are often devoted to schemes for 'improving the welfare of the poor'. A large area is cleared of wretched hovels to make way for the large piles of clean-looking buildings. What has become of the people who were dislodged? Are they re-housed in the new Model Dwellings? Certainly not. In the first place, the rents demanded are too high and in the second place, the caretakers do not select them to live there. It follows that they must drift into other rooms in other houses, perhaps already overcrowded.

The three key questions in the **skills boosts** will help you to generate ideas on how to write about source utility.

1. How do I select criteria for evaluating a source?
2. How do I evaluate the usefulness of a source for a specific enquiry?
3. How do I evaluate the usefulness of a source from what I already know?

Get started

1. Knowledge of the terms used in source analysis, evaluation and judgement will help with this unit. Look at each of the definitions below, then write a summary of each. The first has been done for you.

Term	Definition	Summary
Nature	The form a source takes, such as a photograph, letter, official record or diary.	*Type of source*
Origin	The person who wrote or created a source, where and when they did it.	
Purpose	The reason a source was created, such as to inform, to persuade or to entertain.	
Provenance	The background details about a source, including its nature, origin and purpose (NOP).	
Usefulness	The ways in which a historian could make use of a source for a particular enquiry.	
Reliability	The extent to which a historian could trust a source to reveal the truth about the past.	
Criteria	The means by which a source's usefulness can be measured; reasons for a judgement on its utility (usefulness).	

2. It is helpful to focus on the positives of a source first, before exploring its limitations. Tick which of these statements are positive about Source A.

A. Source A gives an accurate view of the problem of overcrowding in poor districts. ☐

B. The source is a sketch, which may have been drawn to exaggerate the extent of poverty. ☐

C. Source A is from a street in Whitechapel, showing the problems that poverty created there. ☐

D. The source suggests that there was a lot of child poverty. ☐

E. Source A only gives us a picture of the problems on the street, rather than the living conditions inside homes. ☐

The local context of Whitechapel

This unit uses the theme of the local context of Whitechapel to build your skills in evaluating a source's utility by thinking about its provenance, reliability and context. If you need to review your knowledge of this theme, work through these pages.

1 Choose the category A–D that each of the statements in the table belongs to.

A The problem of overcrowded housing

B Attempts to help the poor

C The extent of poverty

D The links between poverty and crime

		A	B	C	D
a	Most people in Whitechapel lived in 'rookeries'.				
b	Conditions in the workhouse were harsh.				
c	In 1875, parliament passed the Artisans' Dwellings Act to start slum clearance.				
d	Overcrowded accommodation increased the chances of theft.				
e	Many people lived in lodging houses, sharing beds in shifts.				
f	Houses were divided into apartments and people were crammed into them.				
g	The Peabody Estate opened in 1881, offering new accommodation for reasonable rents.				
h	Before Dr Barnardo opened his orphanages, most parentless children went to the workhouse.				
i	1,000 people out of the 30,000 in Whitechapel were homeless.				
j	Those who could not care for themselves were sent to the workhouse.				
k	People committed crimes to avoid the workhouse.				
l	Poverty led women to prostitution, putting them at risk of attack.				

2 Write a one-sentence answer for each of the questions below.

a What type of people ended up in the workhouse?

b Why did people hate the workhouse?

c What type of conditions did workers in tailoring, shoemaking and matchmaking work in?

d What problems were caused by reliance on work in railway construction or at the London Docks?

3 Tick the correct answer for each question about housing and overcrowding in Whitechapel.

a How many people might live in one apartment in Whitechapel?

A 10

B 30

C 50

b Which of the following was **not** a problem in lodging houses?

A Rats

B Heat in the summer

C Unaffordable rents

c What sanitation problems did Whitechapel have?

A Limited provision of clean drinking water

B Unavailability of employment

C Overcrowded workhouses

d Why was the Peabody Estate built in Whitechapel?

A To replace slum housing

B To provide housing for wealthier residents

C To increase tourism to London

e What is the term for people, like George Peabody, who fund schemes for the poor?

A Aristocrats

B Legislators

C Philanthropists

4 Draw lines to match each feature of poverty with the specific fact that relates to it.

A Population density	a In 1890 the Houses of the Working Classes Act was passed to replace slums.
B Overcrowding	b The 1881 census records a population of 30,079 people in Whitechapel in 4,069 homes.
C Government help	c Some sweatshop workers were expected to work 20 hours a day.
D Sanitation	d In the 1870s the economy was severely depressed.
E Working conditions	e 200 lodging houses provided beds for 8,000 people.
F Unemployment	f The government passed the Public Health Amendment Act in 1890 to clean the streets and improve toilets.

How do I select criteria for evaluating a source?

In order to evaluate the strength of a source, you need to choose and apply criteria that are relevant to the source, such as how authoritative or typical it is.

Exam-style question

How useful are Sources A and B for an enquiry into the extent of poverty in Whitechapel? **(8 marks)**

1 a Before you can evaluate the strength of a source, you need to consider its provenance (**NOP**). You can use the source details to do this. Source B gives us details of its **N**ature and **O**rigin, but not its **P**urpose. Circle the nature of the source and highlight the origin.

Source B *From a report on sanitary conditions written by Joseph Loane in 1889. Loane was a Medical Officer of Health for the Whitechapel District.*

b Tick the most appropriate purpose in the suggestions below.

- To persuade the government to ban philanthropy ☐
- To report on the living conditions in Whitechapel ☐
- To describe the living conditions of the poor to a friend ☐

2 Consider how much you know about the source to help you choose a criterion from the options in the first column of the table below.

If you know most about...	Choose to evaluate how...	✓
the position or experience of the author/creator	authoritative the source is	
how many people's experiences the source can account for or reflect	typical the source is	
the background and purpose of the source's author/creator	objective or reliable the source is	

3 a Depending on your answer to 2, ask one of the questions below of Source B. Tick your choice.

Criteria	Question to ask of the source	✓
Authoritative	How far does the person who produced the source have the knowledge, or experience, to tell us about the enquiry?	
Typicality	How far does the nature of the source allow us to get a representative view of the enquiry topic?	
Objectivity	How far does the perspective and purpose of the author/creator of the source affect the view it gives on the enquiry topic?	
Reliability	How far can the author/creator of the source be trusted to tell us about the enquiry?	

b Now answer your chosen question. Continue on a separate piece of paper if you need to.

2 How do I evaluate the usefulness of a source for a specific enquiry?

When you look for useful contents in a source, you must consider the topic focus of the enquiry. Then you can think about what strengthens or weakens the usefulness of that content.

Exam-style question

How useful are Sources A and B for an enquiry into the extent of poverty in Whitechapel?

1. Underline the topic focus in the exam-style question.

2. Pick out three pieces of information from Source B (on page 11) and write them into the boxes below. One has been provided for you.

Rich people tried to help the poor. ☐

.... ☐

.... ☐

3. Tick one piece of information from 2 that is related directly to the topic focus. Then make an inference about the topic focus from your choice.

Shows focus on the question	*Source B is useful as it tells us about* ....
Introduces a relevant detail from the source (information)	*because it says/shows* ....
Makes an inference from the detail, suggesting what it can tell us about the topic focus of the enquiry	*This is useful because it suggests* ....

4. Next, you need to consider what you know that strengthens or weakens the usefulness of the contents of the source. Pick one piece of contextual knowledge that suggests your inference is accurate.

1,000 people were homeless in Whitechapel. ☐

The Peabody Estate, opened in 1881, provided new flats at reasonable rents. ☐

Unable to afford their own separate homes, 8,000 people lived in 200 lodging houses in Whitechapel. ☐

5. Continue your answer to 3, using your choice in 4 to strengthen the usefulness of the content you picked out from Source B.

This is an accurate suggestion, because I know that ....

....

....

....

3 How do I evaluate the usefulness of a source from what I already know?

In the process of applying criteria to reach a judgement on the utility of a source, you also need to use your contextual knowledge to consider its provenance.

Exam-style question

How useful are Sources A and B for an enquiry into the extent of poverty in Whitechapel?

1. Write the provenance of Source B into the table.

Nature	
Origin	
Purpose (if clear)	

2. Use the prompts on the spider diagram below to identify some contextual knowledge relevant to the provenance of Source B. Write your knowledge underneath the diagram.

Contextual knowledge to evaluate a source

A How was this type of source produced?

B What do you know about the person, or type of person, who produced the source?

C What do you know about the place and time that the source relates to?

D What do you know about the place and time the source was produced (if different from C)?

E Why do you think this source was produced (its likely purpose)?

3. You can use your contextual knowledge to help evaluate the usefulness of a source.

If you know...	B	...then you can use it in an evaluation of how...	authoritative the source is.
	B or C		typical the source is.
	B, D or E		objective the source is.
	any of them		reliable the source is.

For example, use your knowledge about B to explain why Source B is useful to an historian enquiring into the extent of poverty in Whitechapel.

Get back on track

Sample response

A strong answer to a usefulness question will focus on a specific enquiry and use criteria, supported by contextual knowledge, to evaluate a source. The student answer below does some of these things.

Exam-style question

How useful are Sources A and B for an enquiry into the extent of poverty in Whitechapel?

A Contextual knowledge used to support a claim about a strength of the source for the enquiry.

B Contextual knowledge used to support a claim about a weakness of the source for the enquiry.

C Contextual knowledge used to judge typicality.

Source B is useful for an enquiry about the extent of poverty in Whitechapel because it describes the problem of overcrowding. The Medical Officer says that wretched hovels were cleared, which suggests that there were plenty of them in Whitechapel. This is accurate, as rookeries were common, and could have up to 30 people in one apartment.

Source B's usefulness is strengthened by the fact that it comes from a Medical Officer of Health. More authority can be given to the poverty described in this source, because he was appointed to check on public health. This included the district of Whitechapel, where up to 1,000 people were homeless. However, Source B may not be objective, as Loane may have wanted to improve the conditions in Whitechapel.

D Evaluation of the strengths of the source (how authoritative, typical, objective or reliable it is).

E Evaluation of the weakness of the source.

F Link to the topic focus of the enquiry.

1. The features listed around the student answer relate to the last skills boost. Annotate the answer to show which of these features the student has used in the answer.
2. Which of the features in 1 did the student not use? List them below and suggest how the student could have addressed them in their answer.

Your turn!

Now it's your turn to try to answer an exam-style question.

Exam-style question

How useful are Sources A and B for an enquiry into the extent of poverty in Whitechapel?

1. This chapter has focused on Source B so far. Use the table below to plan a response for Source A on page 11.

What is the topic focus of the enquiry?		Look at the words after 'enquiry' in the exam-style question.
What can you learn from the content of the source?		Pick out content that relates to the topic focus.
What do you know that supports or challenges the accuracy of the contents?		Use own knowledge that links directly to the content you chose.
What does the source caption tell you about its provenance?		What is its NOP?
What do you know about the provenance from your contextual knowledge?		What do you know about this type of source, person, place or time?
How does this affect the strength of the source for the enquiry (refer to criteria)?		Criteria include how authoritative, typical, objective or reliable the source is.

2. Write your paragraph about Source A, using the table plan to structure your response.

Review your skills

Check up

Review your response to the exam-style question on page 19. Tick the column to show how well you think you have done each of the following.

	Had a go	Nearly there	Got it!
selected criteria to evaluate the strengths and weaknesses of the source	☐	☐	☐
focused my analysis and evaluation on the enquiry topic	☐	☐	☐
used my contextual knowledge to evaluate the usefulness of the source	☐	☐	☐

Look over all of your work in this unit. Note down on a separate piece of paper three things you have learned that you will apply when evaluating the usefulness of a source.

Need more practice?

On separate paper, try the exam-style question below.

Exam-style question

Study Sources A and B below.

How useful are Sources A and B for an enquiry into the provision for the poor in the Whitechapel workhouses?

Explain your answer, using Sources A and B and your knowledge of the historical context. **(8 marks)**

Source A *Men in the casual ward of the Whitechapel workhouse on Thomas Street, taken c1902. They are picking apart old rope into raw fibres.*

Source B *From a letter by an inmate at the Whitechapel workhouse at South Grove, written on 19 April 1888. It is an official complaint to the board that supervised the workhouse.*

Just a few lines to let you know how things are carried on at South Grove Workhouse. On Wednesday a man called John Pitkin was held down in the Dining Hall by the Master, the Labour Master and the Asst. Stoker and they took his things away from him. The man was 73 years old and has had heart disease for 34 years and he had a struggle with them in there. There is nothing carried on right in this place. I think the Local Board ought to know how we are treated in the House. We are being treated worse than dogs.

How confident do you feel about each of these **skills**? Colour in the bars.

1. How do I select criteria for evaluating a source?
2. How do I evaluate the usefulness of a source for a specific enquiry?
3. How do I evaluate the usefulness of a source from what I already know?

3 Source enquiry

This unit will develop your ability to follow up a source. The skills you will build are to:

- select detail from a source that is relevant to the topic in the question
- frame a source enquiry question that relates to both the source and the topic in the question
- choose a type of source that supports your planned enquiry question.

In the exam, you will be asked to plan an enquiry based on one source. This unit will prepare you to write your own response to this type of question.

Exam-style question

Study Source A.

How could you follow up Source A to find out more about the effectiveness of policing?

In your answer, you must give the question you would ask and the type of source you could use.

Source A *A cartoon of a scene in the Whitechapel district of London in October 1888. It was printed in* Punch*, a satirical magazine.*

Exam-style question

Study Source B.

How could you follow up Source B to find out more about the working of the Metropolitan Police?

In your answer, you must give the question you would ask and the type of source you could use.

Source B *From an article in* The Nineteenth Century *magazine, 1883. It was called 'Detective Police' and was written by M. Laing Meason.*

A great deal of the crime committed in London meets with the punishment it deserves. Most of the criminals are caught by the ordinary police. Considering the immense districts of houses the force has to watch over, more particularly in many of the suburbs, and taking into consideration how easy of access all our houses are, it is marvellous to note how wonderfully the Metropolitan Police does its duty. It seems little short of a miracle that cases of burglary within the Metropolitan Police district are not twenty times higher than they are.

The three key questions in the **skills boosts** will help you to develop strategies to follow up a source quickly and effectively.

1. How do I decide on a source enquiry?
2. How do I plan a source enquiry?
3. How can I ensure my source supports the question?

Get started

① In the exam, you will be expected to refer to specific sources, such as 'the diary of an inmate at a workhouse in Whitechapel', rather than generic ones, like 'a diary'. Use the spider diagram below to rewrite each of the generic sources in the table as specific ones. One has been done for you.

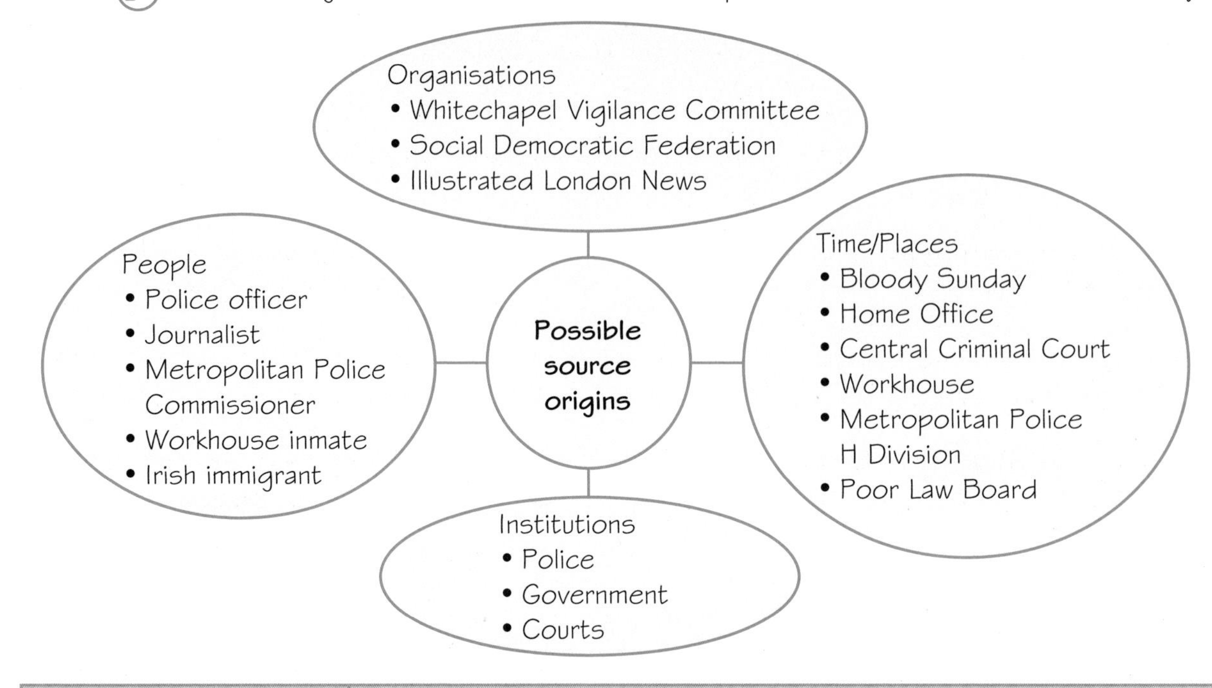

Generic type of source	Specific type of source
Diary	*Diary of an inmate at a workhouse*
Records	
Statistics	
Orders	
Newspaper	
Census	

② The different types of sources, identified in ①, can help in different ways. Match up the type of source to the way it could help an historian.

A Diary	**a** It can give an idea of how common something was.
B Statistics	**b** It can give a view of one person's experience of a situation.
C Report	**c** It can give a view of one person's or team's observations of a situation.
D Newspaper	**d** It can help to reconstruct the jobs and housing conditions of people who lived in a particular place.
E Census	**e** It can give a national, or regional, view of an individual, event or development.

Remember this?

Policing the nation

This unit uses the theme of policing the nation, London and Whitechapel to build your skills in source enquiry. If you need to review your knowledge of this theme, work through these pages.

1 Match up the detail about London to its significance for policing.

Detail	Significance
A There were pockets of serious poverty in London.	a Police had to deal with violent attacks against women.
B Parts of London had a large immigrant population.	b This slowed the rate at which police could respond to a crime.
C There was more than one police force.	c This increased the frequency of crimes such as theft.
D The police forces did not have telephone lines.	d There could be rivalry between forces to catch notorious criminals.
E Some areas had a lot of prostitutes.	e This created tensions that could lead to violence on the streets.

2 Tick whether each of the details in the table relate to the role of the beat constable (A), police commissioner (B) or Home Secretary (C).

	A	B	C
He was supposed to stop to question people.			
Sir Charles Warren, a former general, was appointed to this position in 1886.			
He could act as a poor-relief officer, taking people to the workhouse.			
He had little control over police forces outside of London.			
He used the army to stop the protest in Trafalgar Square on Bloody Sunday.			
He controlled the Metropolitan Police Force, appointing its commissioner.			

3 Answer the multiple-choice questions about the Metropolitan Police and policing in Whitechapel. Tick the correct answer to each.

a In 1885, out of the 13,319 men in the Metropolitan Police, how many were on duty at any one time?

A 13,319

B 1,383

C 10,564

b What was the main job of a constable?

A To run a division of the Metropolitan Police.

B To go out on the beat.

C To stop prostitution, drunkenness and drug abuse.

4 Answer ✓ the multiple-choice questions about the Metropolitan Police and policing in Whitechapel.

a Which division of the Metropolitan Police covered Whitechapel?

A H ☐

B A ☐

C W ☐

b What role did sergeants have in the police force?

A They ran a division. ☐

B They acted as detectives. ☐

C They supervised the work of constables. ☐

c What did Howard Vincent set up in the Metropolitan Police in 1878?

A Fraud Squad ☐

B Special Branch ☐

C Criminal Investigation Department ☐

5 Number the hierarchy of the Metropolitan Police Force from highest (1) to lowest (5).

Superintendent of a division ☐ | Metropolitan Police Commissioner ☐

Home Secretary ☐ | Sergeant ☐ | Constable ☐

6 Complete the text, using words from your own knowledge, about the police force, quality of police recruits and public attitudes towards them.

The .... Police were responsible for most of London's policing. Unlike the rest of Britain's forces, they were run by the government, which had limited funds to pay the police. This meant recruits could be of .... quality and had to be monitored closely by their sergeant.

The public also had concerns about the police. They feared that, like in Europe, the police would .... their liberty. For example, they were used to suppress a popular .... in Trafalgar Square in 1887. They were also seen as supporting unpopular government decisions, making them a target for attacks from violent ....

In especially poor areas such as ...., police performed jobs like controlling prostitution and escorting the poor to .... This created resentment, because people in desperate .... were having their options limited by the police.

How do I decide on a source enquiry?

In a source enquiry, you need to choose a detail from the source that relates to the topic in the question and can be investigated further.

Exam-style question

Study Source A.

How could you follow up Source A to find out more about the effectiveness of policing?

1. The detail you choose must focus on the topic in the question. Highlight the topic in the exam-style question.
2. Annotate the source, labelling any details that relate to the topic in the exam-style question.

Source A *A cartoon of a scene in the Whitechapel district of London in October 1888. It was printed in* Punch, *a satirical magazine.*

FIRST MEMBER OF "CRIMINAL CLASS." "FINE BODY O' MEN, THE PER-LEECE!"

SECOND DITTO. "UNCOMMON FINE! - IT'S LUCKY FOR HUS AS THERE'S SECH A BLOOMIN' FEW OF 'EM!!!"

"I have to observe that the Metropolitan Police have not large reserves doing nothing and ready to meet emergencies; but every man has his duty assigned to him, and I can only strengthen the Whitechapel district by drawing men from duty in other parts of the Metropolis." - *Sir Charles Warren's Statement.* "There is one Policeman to every seven hundred persons." – *Vide Recent Statistics.*

3. Circle any of your annotated details that you think could be investigated further. Consider the questions below to help you decide which to circle. If you can answer 'yes', you could choose that detail to investigate.

? Could your chosen detail lead to an enquiry about the topic?

? Would anyone else have written, photographed or filmed about this detail/a similar detail?

4. a. Write your chosen detail in the table below and explain how it relates to the topic.

Chosen detail	How it relates to the topic

   b. Give an example of another type of person (e.g. journalist, police officer, social researcher) or institution (e.g. government, courts, police) that might have produced a source about this.

2 How do I plan a source enquiry?

In order to plan a source enquiry, you need to frame a question that relates to your chosen detail and the topic stated in the question.

Exam-style question

Study Source A.

How could you follow up Source A to find out more about the effectiveness of policing?

1. a. Highlight the topic in the exam-style question.

   b. One detail from the list below has been ticked as relating to the topic focus in the question. Tick another detail from the list below that relates to the topic and which you want to follow up.

Detail	✓
The police officer has his back turned to the criminals.	
The criminals say there are not many police officers.	✓
The street is well lit.	
The police officer is carrying a truncheon.	
The commissioner says they do not have large reserves of police officers doing nothing.	

2. Write your chosen detail in the table below. Frame a question about your detail, using one of the ideas below or your own. An example is provided.

- How common or typical something was
- Why something was a problem or issue
- How a detail in the source came about
- What the consequences of something were
- The wording of the exam-style question itself

Detail in Source A that I would follow up	Question I would ask
The police officer has his back turned to the criminals.	*How common was it to find police constables missing a crime?*

3. Check that your question meets the criteria below and alter it if necessary.

Checklist	✓
It relates directly to your chosen detail.	
It is about an aspect of the topic in the exam-style question.	
An historian could find out the answer.	

4. Follow the same process using the same source, but for an enquiry about the difficulties of policing the slum area of Whitechapel. Write your chosen detail and question on a separate piece of paper.

3 How can I ensure my source supports the question?

In the process of source selection, you need to choose one that could answer your planned question, revealing something about your chosen detail.

Exam-style question

Study Source A.

How could you follow up Source A to find out more about the effectiveness of policing?

1. A student has chosen a detail and framed their enquiry question for the exam-style question above.

Detail in Source A that I would follow up:	*Question I would ask:*
The criminals say there are not many police officers.	*Was there a connection between police staffing levels and the number of crimes?*

Write three possible sources the student could use to help answer their question. One idea is included below, but there are more on page 22.

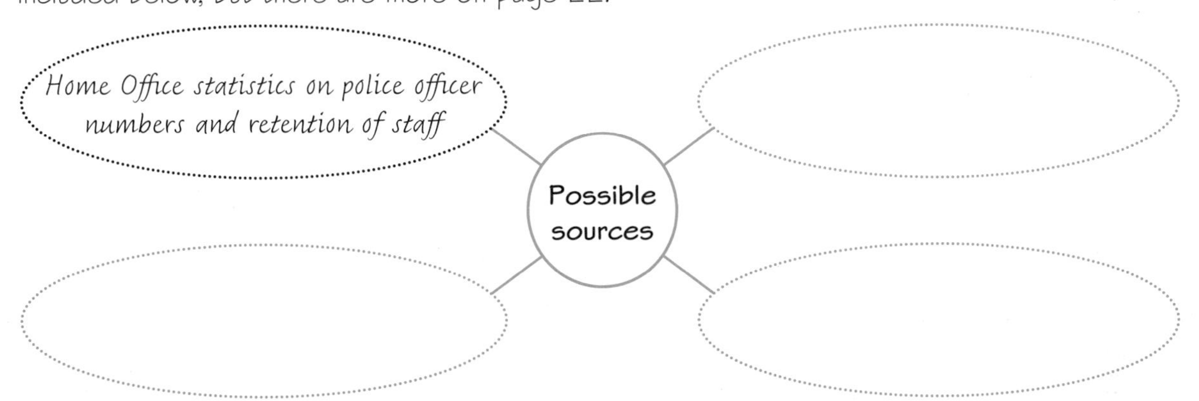

2. Highlight one of your source ideas that could help in one or more of the ways in the checklist below.

Checklist	✓
The source provides more details, rather than repeating those in the supplied source.	✓
It places the chosen detail into a wider context, giving the bigger picture.	✓
It confirms that the detail you have selected gives an accurate impression of the situation.	✓

3. Look at this student's answer, which uses one of the reasons above to say how the source might help answer the question. Try the same thing with the source you highlighted.

What type of source I could use:	*Home Officer reports on police officer numbers.*
How this might help answer my question:	*It could place the detail into the wider context of police officer numbers and staffing problems around the country.*
What type of source I could use:	
How this might help answer my question:	

Sample response

Now you have developed your ability to plan an enquiry and select an appropriate source for it, have a go at assessing a sample student answer.

Exam-style question

Study Source B on page 21.

How could you follow up Source B to find out more about the the working of the Metropolitan Police?

In your answer, you must give the question you would ask and the type of source you could use.

Complete the table below. **(4 marks)**

Detail in Source B that I would follow up:

'great deal of the crime committed in London meets with the punishment it deserves'

Question I would ask:

How did the police help the victims of crime?

What type of source I could use:

Police records

How this might help answer my question:

It might say what the police did for victims.

1 Study the student answer above, then tick ✓ the one thing the student has done correctly.

Checklist	✓
Has the student chosen a detail that relates to the topic in the exam-style question?	
Has the student framed a question that relates to the detail and the topic?	
Has the student chosen a specific source that could help answer their question?	

2 Choose ✓ a valid question that the student could have used instead for their chosen detail.

- How effective were the punishments in reducing reoffending rates? ☐
- What were the consequences of the success of the Metropolitan Police in catching criminals? ☐
- How did the police manage to catch so many criminals? ☐

3 Make the source the student has chosen more specific. ✎

You could add after 'Police records' the words 'from', 'made by' or 'on'.

Police records ....

Your turn!

Now it's your turn to try to answer an exam-style question.

Exam-style question

Study Source B on page 21.

How could you follow up Source B to find out more about the workings of the Metropolitan Police?

In your answer, you must give the question you would ask and the type of source you could use.

Complete the table below. **(4 marks)**

Detail in Source B that I would follow up:

....

Question I would ask:

....

What type of source I could use:

....

How this might help answer my question:

....

① Before you write up your answer in the exam-style question, follow the steps in the planning table below to ensure you write a strong response.

Planning table		
1 What is the topic in the question?		
2 List two to three details in the source that relate to the topic. 3 Highlight one detail that could lead to an enquiry about the topic and which there are likely to be other sources about.		
4 Frame a question that relates to your selected detail, is about an aspect of the topic in the exam-style question and that an historian could answer.		
5 Choose a specific type of source that could provide more details to answer your planned question, place your selected detail in context or confirm the accuracy of the supplied source.		
6 Tick which of these your chosen type of source helps with.	It provides more details to answer your planned question.	
	It places your selected detail in context.	
	It confirms that the detail you have selected gives an accurate impression of the situation.	

② Now write your answer in the spaces in the exam-style question above.

Review your skills

Check up

Review your response to the exam-style question on page 29. Tick the column to show how well you think you have done each of the following.

	Had a go	Nearly there	Got it!
selected a detail that relates to the topic in the exam-style question			
framed a source enquiry question that relates to my chosen detail and the topic in the exam-style question			
chosen a specific type of source that supports my planned source enquiry question			
explained how my source would help answer my question			

Look over all of your work in this unit. Note down three things you have learned that you will apply when following up a source.

1 ....

2 ....

3 ....

Need more practice?

On separate paper, try the exam-style question below.

Exam-style question

Study Source B on page 21.

How could you follow up Source B to find out more about the problem of policing in London?

In your answer, you must give the question you would ask and the type of source you could use.

How confident do you feel about each of these **skills**? Colour in the bars.

1 How do I decide on a source enquiry?

2 How do I plan a source enquiry?

3 How can I ensure my source supports the question?

4 Answering relevantly

This unit will help you to answer a question using relevant material, which is important for all History questions. For a comparison question, it will help you to write a short answer. The skills you will build are to:

- read a question carefully to help identify a relevant point
- select information that supports your point, and is relevant to the topic and the timeframes in the question
- plan an answer, so that your explanation relates to the question.

In the exam, you will be asked to tackle questions such as the ones below. This unit will prepare you to write your own response to this type of question.

Exam-style question

Explain **one** way in which the role of local communities in law enforcement in the medieval period (c1000–c1500) was different from the role of local communities in law enforcement in the nineteenth century. **(4 marks)**

Exam-style question

Explain **one** way in which law enforcement in towns during the sixteenth century was different from law enforcement in towns during the nineteenth century. **(4 marks)**

The three key questions in the **skills boosts** will help you to generate ideas for answering with relevant material.

1. How do I read the question?
2. How do I select relevant information?
3. How do I plan my answer to ensure it answers the question?

Get started

The key to good comparisons is to *explain* them rather than simply *describe* them.

- Describe: give a piece of information about the topic in the question from within the timeframe in the question.
- Explain: make a clear comparison, stating how the two pieces of information are similar or how they differ.

1. Look at the two student answers below. Tick which one describes a difference in the role of local communities in law enforcement between the medieval period and the nineteenth century and which one explains it.

Student answer	Describes	Explains
A *One difference is the level of community involvement. In the medieval period each member of a tithing was responsible for the behaviour of the others, but in the 19th century a professional police force was established. This meant the level of community involvement was reduced.*		
B *In the medieval period, each member of a tithing was responsible for the behaviour of the others. In the 19th century, a professional police force was established.*		

2. For this type of question, you need to use the language of comparison. Highlight the word used to indicate difference in the student answers above. Use the table below to help you.

Similarity words	Difference words
still, remained, continued	but, however, whereas

3. Each student answer below is about a similarity or difference. Cross out ~~cat~~ a word or group of words in each answer and replace them with a word or phrase that more clearly signals a similarity or difference.

A *The hue and cry was raised to catch criminals in the medieval period. Criminals could be caught using the hue and cry in the 16th century.*

B *Men helped to catch criminals in medieval times. They were required to act as constables in the 16th century, with some powers to arrest suspects.*

C *Volunteer night watchmen patrolled towns at night in the 16th century. Robert Peel set up a professional police force in the 19th century.*

D *Coroners were appointed in the 12th century to investigate suspicious deaths. They investigate them in the 21st century.*

E *The police began to keep national crime records in the 19th century. They set up the Police National Computer in the 1970s and 80s.*

F *Professional thief-takers were paid a fee to catch criminals in the 17th century. In the next century some worked for the Bow Street Runners, which the government began to fund in 1785.*

Remember this?

Law enforcement

This unit uses the theme of law enforcement to build your skills in answering relevantly. If you need to review your knowledge of this theme, work through these pages.

1 Sort the answers below into the timeline, which describes the key features of law enforcement between c1000 and the present.

- Edward III appoints Justices of the Peace to act as magistrates and enforce the law.
- The County and Borough Police Act forces all areas to have a police force funded and inspected by the central government.
- The Police National Computer is set up, centralising the records used by the police.
- Women are allowed to become police officers and begin to join police forces.
- The Metropolitan Police Act provides London with a uniformed police force.
- Mounted customs officers are introduced to try to catch smugglers.
- Henry Fielding establishes the Bow Street Runners, using 'Principal Officers' to catch criminals.

Witnesses of a crime raise a hue and cry to catch criminals.	c1000	
	1361	
Town constables and night watchmen become more common figures in towns.	c1500	
	1690	
	1748	
	1829	
	1856	
	c1920s	
	c1970s and 80s	
	1982	*The first Neighbourhood Watch scheme is established, encouraging local residents to be vigilant.*

2 Draw lines linking each law enforcer to the statement that matches their time period.

A Anglo-Saxon tithingman	a I am paid a reward for catching criminals and delivering them to the authorities.
B 16th-century night watchman	b I am a police officer who specialises in tackling drug-trafficking.
C 18th-century thief-taker	c I am responsible for other members of my group, who I have to catch if they are suspected of a crime.
D 21st-century National Crime Agency officer	d I am an unpaid volunteer who patrols the local area between 10pm and dawn.

3 Tick the correct period that each of these statements about the role of local communities and the authorities in law enforcement belong to.

	1000–1500	1500–1700	1700–1900	1900–present
Local officials are renamed constables instead of tithingmen.				
Hue and cry continues to be used, alongside newer practices.				
Soldiers are used to deal with riots.				
Special Branch is set up to investigate terrorists.				
Coroners are appointed to investigate suspicious deaths.				
Town constables are employed by the town authorities.				
Local law enforcers report to the shire reeve.				
Technology such as speed cameras is used to enforce the law.				
Police bicycles and cars are used to catch criminals.				

4 Write definitions of these terms about people and methods used to enforce the law.

a Tithingman: ....

b Hue and cry: ....

c Customs officer: ....

d Principal officer: ....

e Detective: ....

How do I read the question?

For a question about comparison between time periods, you need to pick out the question's key features to ensure you answer it with relevant information and analysis.

Exam-style question

Explain **one** way in which the role of local communities in law enforcement in the medieval period (c1000–c1500) was different from the role of local communities in law enforcement in the nineteenth century. **(4 marks)**

1. First, consider what you are being asked to do. In the exam-style question above:
   a. Underline the command word. *Give*, *describe* or *explain* are used in Paper 1.
   b. Highlight the concept: similarity or difference.

2. Next, work out how much you are supposed to do. Circle the references to the size of the answer.

This could be the number of features you are expected to identify and/or the number of marks the question is worth.

3. Finally, find out what your answer should be about. Annotate the exam-style question identifying:
   a. the topic focus
   b. the timeframes.

Remember, a good answer will:

- focus on the concept
- give information about the topic focus and be within the timeframes
- follow the command word in the exam-style question.

4. Compare the student answers below. Which student has answered the exam-style question correctly?

Student A

One difference was the responsibility of the local community for law enforcement. In the medieval period, the hundredsman and tithingsman were supposed to meet with the king's shire reeve regularly to discuss crime. In the 19th century, it was the responsibility of the local police force to monitor and record criminal activity. This shows a difference, as the local community had less responsibility in law enforcement, which was taken on by the police.

Student B

One difference was the responsibility of the local community for law enforcement. In the medieval period, the hundredsman and tithingsman were supposed to meet with the king's shire reeve regularly to discuss crime. In the twentieth century, there was a range of police departments to enforce the law, such as the Fraud Squad and National Crime Agency. This changed because of developments in government power.

The stronger student answer is ....

because ....

....

....

....

....

How do I select relevant information?

A short-answer question requires you to select precise information that supports your comparison. To do this, it needs to be relevant to the topic and the timeframe.

Exam-style question

Explain **one** way in which the role of local communities in law enforcement in the medieval period (c1000–c1500) was different from the role of local communities in law enforcement in the nineteenth century. **(4 marks)**

1. To unpick the exam-style question, first circle which one of the two concepts in the table applies to the question. Complete the table with the topic focus and timeframes.

Concept:	Similarity / Difference
Topic:	
Timeframe 1:	
Timeframe 2:	

2. Think of some ideas for areas of comparison related to the topic focus. Choose two that are relevant from the list below then write two more.

- methods used to catch criminals ☐
- punishments used ☐
- types of crime committed ☐
- way crime was reported ☐

....

....

3. Highlight one of your areas of comparison from above. Then circle one piece of information that relates to it from each period.

Medieval law enforcement	19th-century law enforcement
One man from each hundred and from each tithing was supposed to meet regularly with the king's shire reeve.	In 1856, the County and Borough Police Act forced the creation of local police forces across the country.
After being caught by the community and tried, criminals could be placed in the stocks.	After being detained by the police and tried, criminals could be sent to prison.
The hue and cry system involved shouting for help, so that everyone who heard could help chase and capture suspects.	Police constables blew a whistle or used a rattle to alert other police officers to help them catch a criminal.

4. Complete the final row of the table (from 3) below, making sure that the second column shows a similarity to or difference from the first.

Medieval law enforcement	19th-century law enforcement
In the 13th century, criminals could be arrested by Justices of the Peace.	

3 How do I plan my answer to ensure it answers the question?

In order to plan a response to ensure it answers the question, you need to identify a point of comparison, support it with evidence and explain how the two things are similar or different.

Exam-style question

Explain **one** way in which the role of local communities in law enforcement in the medieval period (c1000–c1500) was different from the role of local communities in law enforcement in the twentieth century. **(4 marks)**

1. Below is a flow diagram showing the steps you can take when planning an answer to an exam-style question like the one above.

Identify the concept, topic focus and timeframes. → Think of one point of comparison. → Select a piece of information from your own knowledge for each period.

a. Highlight the concept, topic focus and timeframe in the question.

b. Write one point of comparison. ....

c. Write two pieces of supporting information.

....

....

2. Use the thought process above to write a plan for an answer to the exam-style question above.

State one way in which the two timeframes are similar or different.

Identify the first period and give one piece of information.

Identify the second period and give one piece of information.

To complete your answer, you need to explain the similarity or difference. Some ideas that could help build an explanation are shown below.

Similarity: this shows...	Difference: this shows...
the dominance of one idea or institution	a fundamental change in the nature of society
conservative attitudes or values in society	a change in the power of an institution or its approach
lack of progress in technology	a shift of attitudes in society
the continued effectiveness of older methods	advances in technology

3. Now write an explanation for the similarities or differences you wrote in 2.

This shows ....

....

....

....

....

Sample response

Now you have improved your ability to answer a question with relevant detail and explanation, have a go at comparing a weak and a strong student response.

Exam-style question

Explain **one** way in which law enforcement in towns during the sixteenth century was similar to law enforcement in towns during the eighteenth century. **(4 marks)**

Study these two student answers to the exam-style question.

Student 1 (strong)

One similarity between the 16th and 18th centuries was the jobs available in law enforcement. In the 16th century, householders were expected to patrol the streets at night as nightwatchmen. In the 18th century, householders still acted as part-time watchmen and constables. This shows that householders maintained an important role in law enforcement in towns.

Student 2 (weak)

One similarity between the 16th and 18th centuries was the extent of crime linked to towns. In the medieval period, towns had become a popular target for thieves because they were centres for trade. In the 16th century, the crime of vagabondage was introduced and targeted the poor who wandered into towns. It was punished harshly under the Vagrancy Act of 1547 and the 1597 Act for the Relief of the Poor. In the 18th century, another crime was caused by travel between towns. Highway robbery became more common, as people transported their goods and money between towns. To punish it, the death penalty was introduced in 1772. The problems remained the same, because towns were important places.

1. Annotate the strong answer by underlining (A) an example of each of the following features, then writing a label for each underlined section to indicate the feature used.

   A. Makes a comparison focused on the correct concept: similarity or difference.
   B. Uses information from the correct timeframes.
   C. Contains one piece of information from each timeframe in the exam-style question.
   D. Explains briefly how the pieces of information are similar or different.

2. Now underline (A) and annotate the weak answer in the same way. Look out for these mistakes:

   A. The comparison does not focus on the topic in the exam-style question.
   B. It uses irrelevant detail that is outside its timeframe.
   C. It uses irrelevant detail that is unfocused on the exam-style question.
   D. It provides too much detail, rather than selecting it precisely.
   E. It explains why they are similar or different, rather than how.

Your turn!

Now it's your turn to try to answer an exam-style question.

Exam-style question

Explain **one** way in which law enforcement in towns during the sixteenth century was different from law enforcement in towns during the nineteenth century. **(4 marks)**

1. Complete the question analysis table, first circling which one of the two concepts applies to the question. Complete the table with the topic focus and timeframes.

Concept:	Similarity / Difference
Topic:	
Timeframe 1:	
Timeframe 2:	

2. To help keep your answer short and to the point, try writing an answer to the exam-style question by completing the writing frame below. Using the elements you identified in 1, complete the sentence starters.

One way in which (topic focus) .... *was similar/different*

was ....

....

In (period one) ...., *(first detail)* ....,

....

In (period two) ...., *(second detail)* ....

....

This shows ....

....

....

....

....

....

Review your skills

Check up

Review your response to the exam-style question on page 39. Tick the column to show how well you think you have done each of the following.

	Had a go	Nearly there	Got it!
read the question carefully, so my point refers to the correct concept			
selected information that supports my point, is relevant to the topic focus and matches the timeframes in the exam-style question			
planned my answer, so that my explanation shows how the information is similar or different			

Look over all of your work in this unit. Note down three things you have learned that you will apply when answering questions relevantly.

1. ....
2. ....
3. ....

Need more practice?

On separate paper, try the exam-style question below.

Exam-style question

Explain **one** way in which law enforcement in towns during the sixteenth century was different from law enforcement in towns during the twentieth century. **(4 marks)**

How confident do you feel about each of these **skills**? Colour in the bars.

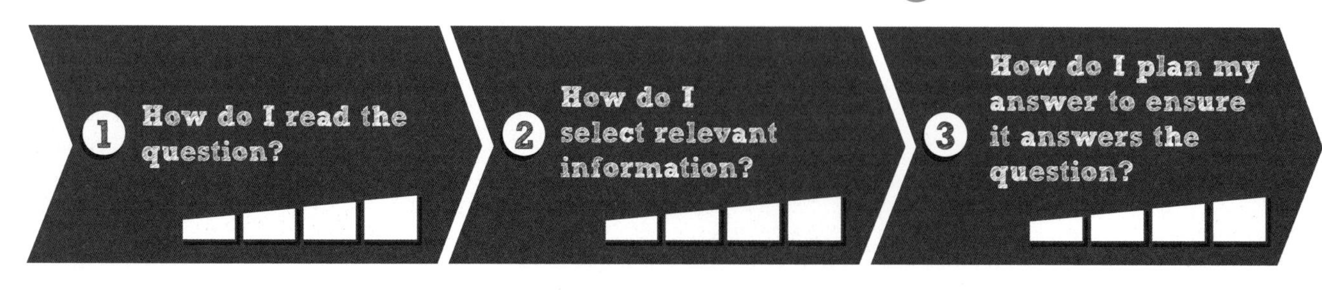

5 Selecting and using supporting evidence

This unit will help you to select and use information precisely in answers focused on causation. The skills you will build are to:

- select information about different aspects of the topic in the question
- check that the information selected can be focused on the concept in the question
- use your own information to show understanding of the characteristics of the period in the question.

In the exam, you need to select and use information precisely. This helps to demonstrate that you have a wide-ranging knowledge of the topic from which you can pick and choose. This unit will help you to prepare your own response to this type of question.

Exam-style question

Explain why there were changes in the use of the death penalty during the period c1900 to the present day.

You may use the following in your answer:

- young offenders
- the Derek Bentley case

You **must** also use information of your own. **(12 marks)**

Exam-style question

Explain why the number of accusations of witchcraft changed quickly during the period c1500–c1700.

You may use the following in your answer:

- witchcraft acts
- the witch hunts of 1645–47

You **must** also use information of your own. **(12 marks)**

The three key questions in the **skills boosts** will help you to improve your ability to select and use information.

How do I select information to answer the question?

How do I ensure that information is relevant to the concept focus?

How do I use my own information?

Get started

To write a strong answer, you need to demonstrate wide-ranging knowledge and understanding. The information you select should be as specific as possible.

1. Link the general information about witchcraft accusations to specific information.

General information	Specific information
A There was a large number of executions for witchcraft from the 16th to the 18th centuries.	a Matthew Hopkins hunted witches in East Anglia between 1645 and 1647.
B The government made it possible to execute witches.	b Between 1542 and 1736, 1,000 people were executed for witchcraft.
C A king wrote about how to catch witches.	c The Act against Conjurations, Enchantments and Witchcrafts was passed to stop minor acts of witchcraft.
D Lots of powerful people acted against witches.	d James I published a book called *Demonologie*, which explained how to conduct a witch trial.
E A new law was passed that undermined the idea of witchcraft.	e In 1542, Henry VIII made witchcraft punishable by death.
F The government passed a law to stop minor acts of witchcraft.	f The Witchcraft Act of 1735 saw witches as confidence tricksters rather than practitioners of black magic.
G A witchfinder stirred up witchcraft accusations.	g Henry VIII, Elizabeth I and James I all passed laws against witches.

2. Identify some examples of specific information from 1 and write them in the table below.

A date: a year that an event, development or individual action took place in.	
An individual or group: a named person, group or institution.	
A named development: a new idea, method or law.	
A statistic: a number of law enforcers, those punished or the cost of something.	

3. The student answer below has used general information to explain why the number of accusations of witchcraft changed quickly. Using specific information shows more knowledge and understanding. Cross out ~~cat~~ any general information and replace it with specific information.

> *One reason the number of accusations of witchcraft changed quickly was that monarchs supported accusations. One king had started the process in the 16th century. Another had made a law that applied to even more people. This led to rapid change because people could now make accusations against witches that the authorities would investigate.*

Witchcraft, heresy and the death penalty

This unit uses the theme of witchcraft, heresy and the death penalty to build your skills in selecting and using supporting evidence. If you need to review your knowledge of this theme, work through these pages.

1. Draw lines to link the events or developments below to their impact on ideas about punishment.

A Timothy Evans was wrongly hanged for murdering his wife and baby in 1950.

B The first borstal was set up in Kent in 1902.

C The Children and Young Persons Act of 1963 raised the age of criminal responsibility to 10.

D Derek Bentley was hanged in 1953, although he did not fire the shot that killed a policeman.

a Support for the death penalty declined.

b Young offenders were viewed as different to other criminals.

2. Were the changes in attitudes above rapid or gradual? Explain why.

....

....

....

....

3. Tick whether these statements about witchcraft and witch hunts are true or false. Cross out (~~cat~~) and correct the false statements.

	Statement	true	false
a	Witches were always tried in Church courts, where the penalties were less severe.	☐	☐
b	Witchcraft accusations were often made by poor individuals against wealthy individuals.	☐	☐
c	James I published *Demonologie*, which explained how to conduct a witchcraft trial.	☐	☐
d	Matthew Hopkins was asked by a JP to search for witches in the West Country.	☐	☐
e	Hopkins accused 117 people of witchcraft in Sudbury.	☐	☐
f	The number of witchcraft accusations grew even higher after Hopkins' death in 1647.	☐	☐

4 Decide whether each of the following is a statement about the crime of heresy or witchcraft. Write H or W in each box.

a They were burned at the stake to purify their soul.

b They were hanged as an example to others.

c The crime was made punishable by death in Henry VIII's reign.

d The crime was made punishable by death in the medieval period.

e A lot of executions for this crime were during the English Civil War.

f To avoid torture, people accused of this crime gave up the names of others involved in it.

g Most executions for this crime were during the reign of Mary I.

h Religious changes increased the fear of people who committed this crime.

i To avoid execution, people accused of this crime could recant.

j Religious changes caused a spike in accusations in the 16th century.

5 Number the following events about changes in punishment, placing them in chronological order.

A The government encourages care orders, supervision and social workers for young offenders.

B 5,000 protestors gather outside Wandsworth Prison as Derek Bentley is executed.

C The death penalty is abolished for most crimes, except for spying, some types of arson and piracy.

D Electronic tagging is used to monitor a criminal's movements.

E A Royal Commission on Capital Punishment is set up.

F Derek Bentley is put on trial for the shooting of a policeman.

G The Criminal Justice Act varies the range of punishments and centres for young people.

H The British government agrees to the 6th protocol of the European Convention on Human Rights, ending the death penalty.

I A national system of borstals is set up under the Prevention of Crime Act.

J The government ends the hanging of under-18s.

How do I select information to answer the question?

To plan a strong answer, you need to select and write about information from at least three aspects of the topic that demonstrate a wide-ranging knowledge of the topic.

Exam-style question

Explain why there were changes in the use of the death penalty during the period c1900 to the present day.

You may use the following in your answer:

- young offenders
- the Derek Bentley case

You **must** also use information of your own. **(12 marks)**

1. Underline the topic focus in the exam-style question above and circle the timeframe.
2. To get a wide range of information, you need to explore different aspects of the topic. Complete the second column in the table below for the other two aspects. One has been done for you.

Generic category	Topic aspect that links to this	Specific information about this aspect
Individuals (Hint: look at the bullet points)	*The Derek Bentley case*	• *Derek Bentley was put on trial for murder in 1952.* • *Bentley had a learning disability.* • *He was executed in 1953 before MPs could pass a motion for a reprieve.*
Attitudes (Hint: look at the bullet points)		
Institutions (Hint: consider what can bring about change)		

3. Add two or three pieces of specific information into the final column of the table.
4. Highlight one specific piece of information in each row, ensuring the three you choose come from different points in the timeframe. This is the evidence you could structure each of your paragraphs around.

2 How do I ensure that information is relevant to the concept focus?

An 'Explain why...' question focuses on the concept of *causation*. This means that the information you select must be able to explain *why* something happened, like change/continuity or slow/rapid change.

Below is a student's plan containing five pieces of information they would like to include in their answer to the exam-style question on page 45.

1. Read the following statements then using the letters Ind (individuals), A (attitudes), Ins (institutions), annotate one statement from each of the following aspects of the topic: individuals, attitudes and institutions.

A 5,000 people protested on the night of Derek Bentley's execution in 1953.
B Young offenders were no longer subject to the death penalty when the hanging of under-18s ended in 1933.
C The Royal Commission on Capital Punishment was set up in 1949.
D The age of criminal responsibility was raised to 10 in 1963.
E The British government agreed to the 6th protocol of the European Convention on Human Rights in 1999.

Try to cover most of the timeframe with your choices.

2. To check that the information you choose is relevant to the concept focus:
   - **a** Underline the concept in the exam-style question: this will always be 'why' for question 4 on Paper 1.
   - **b** Tick what you are being asked to explain from the list.

Checklist Criteria	✓
Why a change occurred	
Why there was rapid/quick change	
Why there was slow/little change	
Why a factor decreased or increased in importance	

Now you know the concept focus, you can check whether the information can address it. The student has tried to do this with aspect C in three different ways.

3. Circle the sentence of explanation that addresses the concept focus you ticked.

Answer 1: This led to rapid change as attitudes towards youth crime shifted at a national level.

Answer 2: This resulted in attitudes towards children becoming more important in determining the punishment given to them.

Answer 3: This meant changing attitudes towards youth crime reduced the range of people to which the death penalty could be applied.

4. Create your own explanation, like the one you circled above, for another piece of information you selected in the list A–E in the student plan.

....

....

Remember: if it cannot be explained in relation to the question, then it is not relevant to the concept focus.

3 How do I use my own information?

To write a high-quality answer, you need to use information of your own about a different aspect of the topic to those suggested by the stimulus bullet points in the exam question.

Exam-style question

Explain why there were changes in the use of the death penalty during the period c1900 to the present day.

You may use the following in your answer:

- young offenders
- the Derek Bentley case

You **must** also use information of your own. **(12 marks)**

1. Underline the topic focus and circle the timeframe in the exam-style question.
2. Write the bullet points from the exam-style question into the table below, alongside the appropriate generic category.

Generic category	Aspect of topic in the exam-style question
Individuals	
Institutions	
Science	
Technology	
Attitudes in society	

3. Add another aspect of the topic to one of the generic categories in the table.
4. You need to ensure that information about your chosen aspect will support your argument. A student has written two examples for the bullet points in the exam-style question. Try doing this with the aspect you added in 3.

The Derek Bentley case	*The Bentley case challenged the morality of the death penalty.*
Attitudes towards young offenders	*People began to see young offenders differently to other criminals.*

5. Now select precisely, from your own knowledge, some specific information to support each point. One has been done for you.

Cause (Point)	Information (Evidence)
The Bentley case challenged the morality of the death penalty.	*Bentley had a mental age of 10, but was executed under joint enterprise law.*

Sample response

A well-written paragraph in a causation essay will use information that has been selected precisely from a wide range of knowledge. Studying the differences between a strong and a weak student answer will help you to write your own.

Exam-style question

Explain why the number of accusations of witchcraft changed quickly during the period c1500–c1700.

You may use the following in your answer:

- witchcraft acts
- the witch hunts of 1645–47

You **must** also use information of your own. **(12 marks)**

1 Read the table below, which describes features of a strong and a weak student answer.

Features of a strong student answer	Features of a weak student answer
Information selected is precise: it is relevant to the point.	Information selected is imprecise: it is only partly relevant to the point.
The concept is focused on: it gives a reason for quick change.	The concept is not focused on: it shows what the changes were, rather than explaining why they happened quickly.

a Underline the precise information in the strong student answer and double underline where the concept is focused on.

b Underline the imprecise information in the weak student answer and double underline where the concept is not focused on.

Student A

One reason the number of accusations of witchcraft changed quickly was that individuals stirred up witch hunts. In 1645 Matthew Hopkins was employed by a JP to uncover witches for financial reward. Hopkins extracted confessions, which named other witches, and searched for physical evidence. As a result, the number of accusations increased because Hopkins used the confessions to find other witches. The change occurred quickly because Hopkins was motivated by the financial reward to accuse more witches.

Student B

One reason the number of accusations of witchcraft changed was the work of Matthew Hopkins. He searched for witches in England, using local gossip, physical investigations and forced confessions. This shows that there were a lot of ways to catch witches. This caused the number of accusations to change quickly.

c Using your answers to **a** and **b**, explain which student answer is stronger and why.

Your turn!

This unit has focused on planning an answer. Now it's your turn to try to plan an answer to an exam-style question.

Exam-style question

Explain why the number of accusations of witchcraft changed quickly during the period c1500–c1700.

You may use the following in your answer:

- changes in religion
- the work of Matthew Hopkins

You **must** also use information of your own. **(12 marks)**

1 a To start the planning process, one of the bullet points from the exam-style question has been added to the table below. Write the remaining bullet point in the appropriate place in the second column, then add a topic aspect of your own alongside the relevant generic category.

Generic category	Aspect of topic in the question	Specific information
Individuals		
Institutions		
Science		
Technology		
Attitudes in society	*Changes in religion*	

b Add one piece of specific information to each of your topic aspects.

c Check your specific information meets each of the criteria in the checklist below. Add more detail to the table in a if it does not.

Checklist	✓
They each cover a different aspect of the topic in the question.	
They give specific details, such as dates, individuals, named developments or statistics.	
They each come from a different point in the timeframe.	

d Identify the concept in the exam-style question. In the list below, tick what you are being asked to explain. Then tick each of your three pieces of specific information in the table in a to confirm they focus on this.

Why a change occurred	☐	Why there was slow/little change	☐
Why there was rapid/quick change	☐	Why a factor decreased or increased in importance	☐

2 Turn your information into a plan. Write three causes (points) in answer to the exam-style question that each piece of information in your table could support.

Cause (Point)	Information (Evidence)

Review your skills

Check up

Review your response to the exam-style question on page 49. Tick the column to show how well you think you have done each of the following.

	Had a go	Nearly there	Got it!
selected information precisely to support the points I have made			
ensured that the information is used to explain why something happened			
used my own information to enhance my explanation, showing I understand the characteristics of the period			

Look over all of your work in this unit. Note down three things you have learned that you will apply when selecting and using supporting evidence.

1. ....
2. ....
3. ....

Need more practice?

On separate paper, try the exam-style question below.

Exam-style question

Explain why the number of accusations of heresy changed quickly during the period c1500–c1600.

You may use the following in your answer:

- the Reformation
- the reign of Mary I

You **must** also use information of your own. **(12 marks)**

How confident do you feel about each of these **skills**? Colour in the bars.

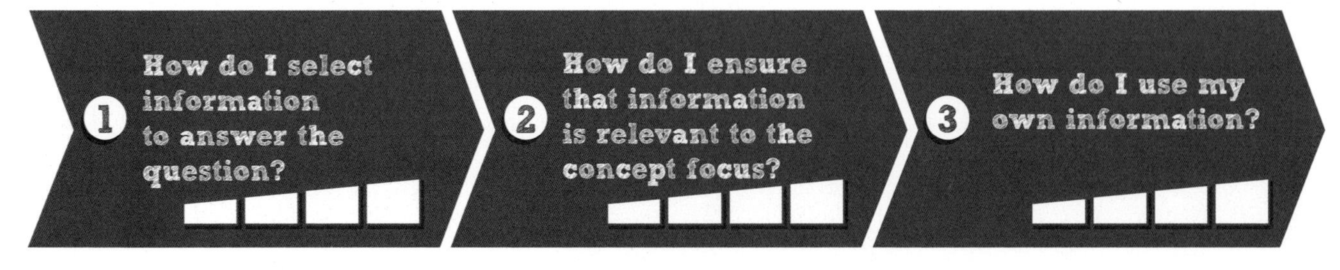

6 Analysing causation

This unit will help you to plan and write better arguments when you are working on causation essays, which explain why an event or development occurred. The skills you will build are to:

- identify causes that relate to the question
- use knowledge to strengthen your arguments
- make effective links back to the question.

In the exam, causation can appear in questions 4, 5 and 6. However, causation will *always* be the focus of question 4. This unit will prepare you to write your own response to this type of question.

Exam-style question

Explain why the influence of the Church on law enforcement changed slowly in the period c1000–c1250.

You may use the following in your answer:

- trial by ordeal
- the benefit of clergy

You **must** also use information of your own. **(12 marks)**

The three key questions in the **skills boosts** will help you to write a strong causation argument.

1. How do I build a causal argument?
2. How do I support my causal argument with my own knowledge?
3. How do I link my causal argument back to the question?

Get started

The focus of this unit is on improving your causal arguments. This will enable you to build on your understanding of good paragraph structure in order to write a strong causation essay.

1. Draw lines linking the paragraph feature to its purpose in a causal argument.

A Point	a Explore how the evidence proves the point it supports.
B Evidence	b Link back to the question, explaining how the cause analysed in the paragraph relates to the question.
C Explanation	c Introduce the cause, providing an answer to the question.
D Link	d Supporting knowledge that can prove the point being made.

This unit will refer to a number of terms used to describe the components of a causation essay. These are:

A Topic focus: the topic in the question.

B Cause: the reason something occurred.

C Precise information: facts, figures and dates.

D Contextual knowledge: background information about the period, country or world view.

E Link: a connection between causes, or between a cause and the thing you are trying to explain.

2. Referring to the exam-style question on page 51, label each of the statements below with the appropriate term, A–E, from the list above.

a The Church administered trial by ordeal. ☐

b Influence of the Church on law enforcement. ☐

c Attitudes in society. ☐

d Most people accepted the Church's teachings. ☐

e Conservative attitudes caused people to trust the Church to judge criminals, rather than rely on other methods. ☐

Remember this?

Crime and punishment in medieval England

This unit uses the theme of crime and punishment in medieval England to build your skills in analysing causation. If you need to review your knowledge of this theme, work through these pages.

1 In the table below, look at the list of medieval methods of law enforcement. Tick which category each method belongs in.

	Trial by ordeal	Trial by combat	Judgement by community
A The accused could be burned and judged on how well the wound healed.			
B The accused could swear their innocence under oath.			
C The accused could be thrown into cold water and judged guilty if they floated.			
D The Normans introduced this type of trial.			
E A priest would organise the trial.			
F Minor crimes were dealt with in a manor court.			
G The accused fought the accuser.			
H Repeat offenders were not allowed to take an oath of innocence.			
I A champion could fight on behalf of the accuser.			
J A priest could undertake a trial by consecrated bread and would be judged guilty if he choked.			
K It was believed God would help strengthen the accused if they were innocent.			
L Local Justices of the Peace were appointed by the monarch after 1361.			

2 Draw lines linking each idea about crime to the method of law enforcement used.

A Local communities had collective responsibility for law enforcement.

B God could judge the accused directly.

C The monarch was a powerful figure.

D The Church had a role in controlling behaviour.

a The accused could undergo a trial either by ordeal or by combat.

b In a serious criminal case the accused could be judged by Justices in Eyre.

c The accused could swear an oath of innocence.

d A person accused of a moral crime or heresy could be tried by the Church court.

3. Complete the text about the role of the Church in law enforcement, using the letter hints to help you.

The Church was a very powerful institution. There were churches in most villages and the Church owned a huge amount of land. It was also r..............................., as one-tenth of a person's earnings was given to the Church as a t............................... As a result, the Church accounted for about one-fifth of England's wealth.

Another power the Church had was over a person's behaviour. People were expected to confess their sins to the Church. A priest would prescribe a punishment, or p..............................., for the sinner to undertake. For more serious m............................... crimes, like those related to marriage, the Church court could hear evidence and give a punishment. Their punishments could be harsh, but not as severe as those in the king's court.

Finally, the Church had a lot of privileges. If you were a cleric and committed a crime, you could ask for 'b............................... of clergy', which meant that your case would be heard in a Church court. Henry II tried, unsuccessfully, to limit this power. A church could also be a place of refuge and any criminal could go to one and ask for s............................... This meant they would be protected inside the church and could swear an oath agreeing to leave the country without fear of arrest.

4. Identify the type of authority that each of the people in the table would be most likely to visit during the medieval period. Choose from the following options.

King's shire reeve | Local lord | The bishop | A priest | Members of tithing group

Who would you go to if you...	Authority figure
A heard the hue and cry because a criminal in your tithing group was trying to escape the law?	
B needed to bring a criminal in your tithing group to justice?	
C needed God to judge whether someone was guilty or not?	
D wanted someone to deliver justice on a local matter?	
E had committed a moral crime and were a member of the clergy?	

5. The local community was important in law enforcement. Tick whether the following statements about it are true or false.

	Statement	true	false
a	Members of a tithing were responsible for each other's behaviour.	☐	☐
b	To prove their innocence to their neighbours, a criminal could swear an oath of innocence, even if they were caught 'red-handed'.	☐	☐
c	If an Anglo-Saxon murdered a Norman, but the murderer was not found, the tithing had to pay a murdrum fine.	☐	☐
d	The hue and cry was an Anglo-Saxon practice that the Normans stopped.	☐	☐
e	Henry II's judges heard the most serious criminal cases once a month.	☐	☐

How do I build a causal argument?

In order to build a causal argument, you need to identify causes that answer the question. These should address the topic focus and the process of change in the question.

Exam-style question

Explain why the influence of the Church on law enforcement changed slowly in the period c1000–c1250.

1. The first step is to understand what it is you need to explain. Underline the topic focus and circle the process of change you need to explain in the exam-style question above.
2. Next you need to consider which areas, or aspects, of the topic focus need to be explored to explain the process of change. One has been identified for you in the table below. Write two more.

Different areas or aspect of focus	A *The Church dealt with moral crimes.*
	B
	C

3. Once you understand the focus, aim to come up with three different causes of the process of change. To do this, combine the focus and process into an exam-style question statement and write them below. The first one has been done for you.

To help you combine process and focus, follow this formulation:

- Explain why there was [process] in [aspect of focus]...

a *Explain why there was slow change in the Church's power to deal with moral crimes.*

b ....

c ....

4. You should now provide the opening point for each of your paragraphs by answering your questions above. One has been done for you.

a *The influence of the Church changed slowly because the Church had a lot of control over people's behaviour.*

b ....

c ....

5. Three students have given the answers below. However, only one addresses the focus and concept in the exam-style question. Circle the correct one.

Medieval people respected the authority of their monarch.

Some kings gave the Church control over aspects of law enforcement.

There were new laws introduced during the medieval period that applied to clerics.

2 How do I support my causal argument with my own knowledge?

In a well-written essay, knowledge will be selected precisely to support the point you are making. It can then be explained to help validate your point.

Exam-style question

Explain why the influence of the Church on law enforcement changed slowly in the period c1000–c1250.

Relevant knowledge will link directly to the point you are making. Two points in answer to the exam-style question are given below.

1. Add your own evidence for the second point in the plan.

If you struggle with this process, return to Unit 5 and review what you learned there.

Point	Evidence
A The Church had a strong influence on people's behaviour.	One-tenth of all earnings were paid to the Church as a tithe.
B The Church had a lot of power.	

To use knowledge in an analytical way, it should be connected to your point. One way to do this is to use part of the wording of your point in the same sentence as your knowledge.

2. Look at the student answer below, which uses point A. Highlight the phrase that connects the point and the knowledge.

One reason the influence of the Church on law enforcement changed slowly was that the authorities sometimes relied on it. If a trial by ordeal was used, the authorities relied on the Church to administer the trial, which was organised by priests.

3. Using point B, write a sentence that links to the evidence you wrote in 1. Use a different phrase from the one in the student example above.

....

....

Your knowledge should prove a point and be followed by an explanation of how it proves this point. In a sophisticated analysis, knowledge often forms part of the explanation too.

4. Look at the student response below for a different point.
   - a) Underline the point (cause).
   - b) Circle the knowledge relating to the point.
   - c) Double underline the explanation of how the knowledge proves the point.

One reason the influence of the Church changed slowly was that the authorities sometimes relied on it. For example, Anglo-Saxon justice relied on an oath made to God by the accused to swear their innocence. If they lied, the Church taught that they would be punished by God. This meant an important way that people received justice, by swearing an oath of innocence, was backed up by Church teaching.

5. On a separate piece of paper, using your work from activities 1–3, write point B, supported by your own knowledge, which you should explain.

3 How do I link my causal argument back to the question?

A strong causal argument will link back to the key words in the question at the end of each paragraph. This will build up your line of reasoning, showing the relevance of your ideas to the question.

Exam-style question

Explain why the influence of the Church on law enforcement changed slowly in the period c1000–c1250.

1. In the student's answer below,
   - a. circle (A) where they have identified the topic and concept focus
   - b. underline (A) where they have provided a reason in answer to the question
   - c. double underline (A) where they have presented their own knowledge
   - d. highlight where they have explained how their knowledge proves their point.

One reason there was slow change in the influence of the Church on law enforcement was that the Church protected its own power. The Church had the power to judge criminals who were also clerics. When Henry II tried to take this power away in the 1160s, the Church resisted him. This meant it kept the power of 'benefit of clergy'. This led to slow change in the Church's influence on law enforcement, because the king struggled to take power away from it.

The final stage in the construction of a paragraph is to link back to the question, explaining how a part of the focus (treatment) and process (changed slowly) came about.

2. Annotate the link in the student answer in 1.
3. Write your own link back to the exam-style question for the paragraph below.

One reason the influence of the Church changed slowly was that the authorities sometimes relied on it. For example, Anglo-Saxon justice relied on an oath made to God by the accused to swear their innocence. If they lied, the Church taught that they would be punished by God. This meant an important way that people received justice, by swearing an oath of innocence, was backed up by Church teaching. It led to slow change in the influence of the Church on law enforcement because ....

....

....

....

4. Another type of link back to the question is one that links the cause you have just discussed to another one in your essay. Write a link between the second student paragraph about the reliance of the authorities on the Church to the first about Church protection of its power.

The Church's desire to protect its own power along with the reliance of the authorities on the Church combined to bring about slow change in its influence because ....

....

....

....

....

Sample response

It helps to know what a strong answer looks like, so that you can check whether your causation essays build effective arguments.

Read the following exam-style question and then look at the extract from a student answer.

Exam-style question

Explain why the influence of the Church on law enforcement changed slowly in the period c1000–c1250.

You may use the following in your answer:

- trial by ordeal
- the benefit of clergy

You **must** also use information of your own. **(12 marks)**

One reason why approaches to law enforcement changed slowly was that the Church was a very powerful institution. It could judge criminals in a trial by ordeal. This meant that trials to judge the accused, such as those by hot iron or cold water, were controlled by the Church. This led to slow change because this type of trial was used by both Anglo-Saxons and Normans, who relied on the Church to judge criminals throughout the period, reinforcing the Church's power.

1. The strongest features of the student answer have been highlighted, using four different colours. Write which colour represents which feature of the causal argument.

Point .... Knowledge ....

Explanation .... Link back to the question ....

It is important to remember that more than one piece of knowledge could support the same point. This should help you focus your revision on a few pieces of detailed knowledge for each topic.

2. Tick an additional piece of knowledge from the table below for the student answer.

Trial by ordeal ended in 1215.	☐
There were a lot of churches in England.	☐
The Church had its own courts.	☐

3. Highlight one reason why the link back to the question strengthens the paragraph.

- It introduces the knowledge you used.
- It provides essential information to prove the point.
- It helps to build up your overall argument.

Your turn!

Using the skills you have developed over this unit, you are now going to plan and write your own answer to the exam-style question below.

Exam-style question

Explain why the influence of the Church on law enforcement changed slowly in the period c1000–c1250.

You may use the following in your answer:

- trial by ordeal
- the benefit of clergy

You **must** also use information of your own. **(12 marks)**

1 Complete the table below with your own ideas for how to answer the exam-style question above.

Point	
Supporting knowledge	
Explanation	
Link back to the question	

2 Use the checklist to review your planned paragraph.

Checklist **Have you:**	✓
chosen a point that refers to a cause in answer to the question?	
used supporting knowledge linked to your point?	
explained how your supporting knowledge proves your point?	
explained your link back to the question, developing your overall argument?	

3 Write your paragraph on a separate piece of paper. Remember to:

- connect your point and knowledge together
- use more knowledge in your explanation, if it helps strengthen it
- refer to circumstances, a key part of the process and focus, or link to another cause in your link back to the question.

Review your skills

Check up

Review your paragraph response to the exam-style question on page 59. Tick the column to show how well you think you have done each of the following.

	Had a go	Nearly there	Got it!
chosen a cause that relates directly to the focus and process in the question			
used knowledge to strengthen the argument			
written a link that builds up my overall argument in response to the question			

Look over all of your work in this unit. Note down three things you have learned that you will apply when organising your causal arguments.

1 ....

2 ....

3 ....

Need more practice?

On separate paper, try the exam-style question below.

Exam-style question

Explain why the role of the local community in law enforcement changed slowly in the period c1000–c1250.

You may use the following in your answer:

- the hue and cry
- the murdrum fine

You **must** also use information of your own. (12 marks)

How confident do you feel about each of these **skills**? Colour in the bars.

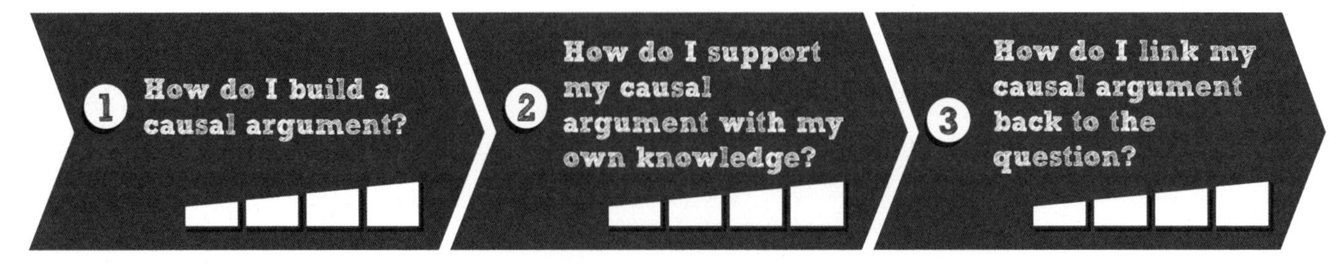

Get started

7 Understanding change and continuity

This unit will help you to plan and write answers to questions focused on change and continuity. The skills you will build are to:

- identify changes in a given topic over a specified timeframe
- evaluate whether an event, development or individual's work is a turning point in history
- evaluate the extent of change in a given topic over a specified timeframe.

In the exam, the 'how far do you agree' question could focus on the nature or extent of change, patterns of change, the process of change or the impact of change. This unit will help you to write a response to the first two types of question.

Exam-style question

'The end of transportation was a turning point in the methods used to punish criminals in the period c1800 to the present day.'

How far do you agree? Explain your answer.

You may use the following in your answer:

- ending transportation to Australia
- abolition of the death penalty

You **must** also use information of your own. **(16 marks)**

Exam-style question

'There was huge change in the definition of criminal activity in the period c1500–c1700.'

How far do you agree? Explain your answer.

You may use the following in your answer:

- laws against heresy
- vagabonds

You **must** also use information of your own. **(16 marks)**

The three key questions in the **skills boosts** will help you to generate ideas to plan an essay focused on change and continuity.

How do I identify change?

2 **How do I evaluate whether something is a turning point?**

How can I evaluate the extent of change?

Get started

In this unit you will focus on how to construct a plan for an essay about change and continuity. However, to write this up, you still need to follow the correct paragraph structure.

1. Choose ✓ the best description of the role of each of these features in a strong paragraph.

Feature	Descriptions to choose from	Best description ✓
Point	To open a paragraph, focusing on one aspect of the question.	
	To open a paragraph with some description relevant to the question.	
Evidence or knowledge	To support your point with anything you can remember about the topic.	
	To support or illustrate your point with precisely selected information.	
Explanation	To explain how your information proves the point you are making.	
	To give a bit more detail about the information you have selected.	
Link back to the question	To build up your overall argument in relation to the question set.	
	To repeat, or paraphrase, the words of the question.	

Look at the student paragraph below, which is part of an answer to an exam-style question about the extent of change.

Exam-style question

'There was huge change in the definition of criminal activity in the period c1500–c1700.'

How far do you agree? Explain your answer.

There was a huge change in the government's attitude towards crime. England's population was growing, which resulted in a fall in wages and a rise in the cost of living. This meant that there were more homeless people without a job moving from place to place, which the government saw as a threat. So the government made vagrancy a serious crime in 1547. This led to a huge change in the definition of criminal activity, because the nationwide problem of vagrancy meant that the government saw it as a threat and turned it into a crime in both rural and urban communities.

2. a. Highlight where a point has been made.
   b. Underline where evidence has been given.
   c. Circle where an explanation has been made.
   d. Double underline where the student has linked back to the question.

3. The student has also begun to use the language of continuity and change. Label the student answer with any references to the following elements of change, using the words in bold as your labels. You may not find them all.

A. the **scale** of change: how far-reaching a change is, whether local, national or international

B. a **trend**: a group of similar changes continuing in the same direction

C. **extent** of change: how big or small the change is

D. the **direction** of change: the way change is heading, whether towards a situation improving or getting worse

Remember this?

Crime c1500–c1700 and punishment c1800–present

This unit uses the theme of crime, c1500–c1700, and punishment, c1800 to the present day, to build your skills in understanding change and continuity. If you need to review your knowledge of this theme, work through these pages.

1 Answer the questions about definitions of crime and punishment between c1500 and c1700.

a How did Cromwell change the crime of recusancy?

A He decriminalised it.

B He increased fines for it.

C He reintroduced the death penalty for it.

b What did the crime of treason become associated with in the 16th century?

A Heresy

B Hunting

C Vagabondage

c Which statement best describes the Vagrancy Act of 1547?

A It left the Church to deal with vagrants.

B It strengthened the penalty for vagrancy, but it was only in force for three years.

C It created the crime of vagrancy and it was in force until the 1597 Act.

d What did the Game Act of 1671 make illegal?

A Gambling in alehouses

B Hunting in the Royal Forest

C Hunting on enclosed land

e How did the Witchcraft and Conjuration Act change the definition of witchcraft?

A It viewed witches as confidence tricksters.

B It extended the death penalty to those summoning evil spirits.

C It made it an offence to be tried in the Church court.

2 Complete the sentences, giving a brief explanation of the significance of each of the laws in 1.

a *The association of treason with* .... *meant that* ....

b *The Vagrancy Act of 1547 was not significant in the short term because* ....

c *The Game Act meant that crimes related to* ....

d *The extension of the definition of witchcraft was significant because it meant* ....

3. Draw lines to link each change in crime and punishment to its cause.

A Australia was seen as a good place to live because gold was discovered there.

B Crowds at an execution saw it as a fun spectacle.

C By 1810, 222 crimes were capital offences, and juries were often reluctant to give guilty verdicts.

D In the mid-19th century, many people thought prison should deter others from crime.

E In the late 19th century, many people thought prison should rehabilitate a criminal.

F Robert Peel advocated a system to reform prisons in the 1820s.

a Public executions stopped in 1868.

b The 1865 Prisons Act ensured prisoners had to perform hard labour in tough conditions.

c The decline of the Bloody Code.

d Transportation ended in 1868.

e The 1823 Gaols Act ensured that gaolers were paid and conditions improved.

f The practice of hard labour in prisons ended in 1902.

4. Cross out the incorrect information in each of these statements and write your own corrections on the line underneath. They are about methods used to punish criminals between c1900 and the present day and they are in chronological order.

a The first open prison was established in 1933 to punish criminals severely.

....

b During the Second World War, conscientious objectors were treated harshly by the authorities.

....

c Alexander Patterson, a prisons commissioner, campaigned for restorative justice.

....

d In 1965, the home secretary, Roy Jenkins, ended transportation.

....

e To monitor convicts outside of prison, mobile phones were used to track them.

....

f Anti-Social Behaviour Orders were introduced to force criminals to do hard labour.

....

How do I identify change?

For a question about change and continuity, you need to identify what has changed over the period. This will help to provide evidence for the points in your argument.

Exam-style question

'The end of transportation was a turning point in the methods used to punish criminals in the period c1800 to the present day.'

How far do you agree? Explain your answer.

1. Underline the topic focus in the exam-style question above and highlight the timeframe.
2. Summarise the state of affairs in the topic focus at the start and end of the period.

At the start of the period, methods used to punish criminals ....

At the end of the period, methods used to punish criminals ....

3. Add four events, developments or the works of individuals to the table below that could have contributed to the difference described in 2. Some things that you should look for are:

- ? changes in technology
- ? new ideas from, or actions of, individuals
- ? shifts in attitudes
- ? examples of weakening or strengthening institutions

Transportation was seen as an attractive punishment by some.	*Robert Peel's penal reforms in the 1820s.*	

4. Ask yourself questions 1–3 again, this time focusing on changes in 'the definition of criminal activity in the period c1500–c1700'. Work through the stages on paper and then write the six changes you have decided on in the space below.

2 How do I evaluate whether something is a turning point?

To construct a plan for an essay focused on patterns of change, you need to apply criteria to decide whether an event, individual's work or development is a turning point.

Exam-style question

'The end of transportation was a turning point in the methods used to punish criminals in the period c1800 to the present day.'

1. Underline the topic focus, highlight the timeframe and circle the turning point provided in the exam-style question.

2. Complete the before and after table to help you analyse the turning point provided in the exam-style question. The before side has been done for you.

Before the turning point	After the turning point
a Convicts were transported to Australia as a punishment.	
b Prisons were not designed to hold a lot of prisoners.	
c Criminals could be sentenced to death.	

3. Apply criteria to help judge whether an event is a turning point. Complete the table below, relating the generic criteria to the specific turning point in the exam-style question.

Did it affect the pace of change?	
Evidence that the pace of change sped up	Evidence that the pace of change slowed down or stayed the same
Did it break with a trend?	
Evidence that it was a major disruption in a trend	Evidence that it was part of a trend of similar changes (list other events/developments that affected the topic in the question)
Did it lead to a significant amount of change?	
Evidence that it led to significant change	Evidence that other turning points were more significant

4. Turn the findings in your table into two opening statements for paragraphs in an essay by completing the sentences below.

An argument that the end of transportation was a turning point was that ....

Did it speed up change?

However, it may not have been a turning point, as ....

Did anything stay the same?

3 How can I evaluate the extent of change?

In order to evaluate how much has changed over a period of time, you need to identify what has changed and then use criteria to evaluate the changes.

Exam-style question

'There was huge change in the definition of criminal activity in the period c1500–c1700.'

How far do you agree? Explain your answer.

1. Underline the topic focus and highlight the timeframe in the exam-style question.

2. Complete the table to help you identify what changed between the start and end of the timeframe in the exam-style question above. Your points should relate to the topic focus.

State of affairs c1500	State of affairs c1700
	Vagabondage was treated as a serious crime for which people were sent to houses of correction.
	Witchcraft was dealt with by the common court and the death penalty could be given to those found guilty of it.
	Holding a different religious belief was no longer a crime, but still led to social and political restrictions.

3. Use the questions below to help you judge the extent of change during the timeframe. Circle the appropriate options in the table to answer each question.

   a. What was the scale of the change? Local | National | International

   b. How much change was there in people's attitudes and the role of institutions?

   Significant change | Partial change | No change

   c. Draw an arrow on the value continuum below to show how much continuity there was between the start and end of the period.

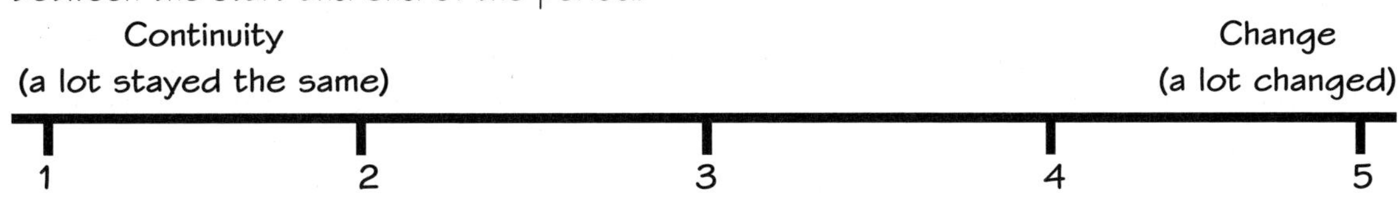

4. Use your ideas in the table in 2 to help you complete the sentences below, which could form the plan for an essay about extent of change.

   a. *The scale of change during this period was* ....

   b. *During the period there was* ....

   c. *Overall, there was* .... *continuity between the start and end of the period.*

Sample response

The ability to evaluate a turning point is vital in an essay focused on patterns of change. Seeing the strengths in a strong student answer will help you when writing your own.

Exam-style question

'The introduction of the new crime of vagabondage was a turning point in the definition of criminal activity in the period c1500–c1700.'

How far do you agree? Explain your answer.

Study these two paragraphs, which are part of a strong student answer to the exam-style question above.

The new crime of vagabondage led to significant change, as poverty was now seen as a serious crime rather than a social problem. Before the mid-16th century, vagabondage had been treated as a social problem, which the community that the poor person came from would have to deal with. During the Tudor period, new legislation, like the Vagrancy Act of 1547, distinguished between the deserving poor and sturdy beggars. This meant some forms of poverty were clearly defined as criminal. This made the new crime of vagabondage a turning point because the government turned a method of survival for the able-bodied poor into a criminal activity, for which increasingly harsh punishments were given.

However, the new crime of vagabondage was also part of a trend in widening the definition of what the state considered to be a crime. In the 16th century, new laws were passed to make witchcraft illegal, such as the 1542 Witchcraft Act. This continued in the 17th century, when James I widened the definition of practices associated with witchcraft. Both of these developments meant that the state was defining crimes to control people's behaviour and did so throughout the period. This suggests the new crime of vagabondage was less of a turning point, because it was part of a trend towards criminalising certain behaviours.

1. Identify the skills the student has demonstrated. To do this:
   - a. Highlight changes they have used as evidence: events, developments or the works of individuals.
   - b. Underline criteria for a turning point: change in pace, direction of change or disruption of a trend.
   - c. Circle references to the extent of change: scale of impact, level of continuity or progress in attitudes, power or knowledge.
2. The student has demonstrated good understanding of change and continuity, but complete the checklist below to find out how well they have structured their paragraph.

Checklist	✓
Does it focus on the topic?	
Is the evidence from within the timeframe?	
Does the line of reasoning, developed in the link back to the question, relate to whether the turning point mentioned in the question is actually a turning point?	

Your turn!

Now it's your turn to try to answer an exam-style question.

Exam-style question

'The abolition of the death penalty was a turning point in the methods used to punish criminals in the period c1800 to the present day.'

How far do you agree? Explain your answer.

You may use the following in your answer:

- abolition of the death penalty
- construction of Pentonville Prison

You **must** also use information of your own. **(16 marks)**

The flow chart below will help you to construct a plan for the exam-style question.

Identify the topic focus, timeframe and proposed turning point in the question. → Make a list of the state of affairs before and after the turning point. → Apply criteria to help generate points about whether it was a turning point (consider whether other developments were more significant). → Did it affect the pace of change? Did it break with a trend (consider the whole period)? Did it affect the direction of change?

1. Write the four points you would make in your essay, each of which could start a paragraph in answer to the exam-style question.

   1 ....

   2 ....

   3 ....

   4 ....

2. Write one of your paragraphs, remembering to structure it around a point, supported by evidence, which you explain and then link back to the question.

....

....

....

....

....

....

....

....

....

Review your skills

Check up

Review your response to the exam-style question on page 69. Tick the column to show how well you think you have done each of the following.

	Had a go	Nearly there	Got it!
followed a clear paragraph structure, including changes as part of my evidence	☐	☐	☐
focused on the topic, timeframe and turning point in the question	☐	☐	☐
developed a line of reasoning related to whether the suggested turning point in the question was actually a turning point	☐	☐	☐

Look over all of your work in this unit. Note down three things you have learned that you will apply when answering questions focused on change and continuity.

1 ....

2 ....

3 ....

Need more practice?

On separate paper, try the exam-style question below.

Exam-style question

'There was huge change in the methods used to punish criminals in the period c1800 to the present day.'

How far do you agree? Explain your answer.

You may use the following in your answer:

- the introduction of the separate system
- open prisons

You **must** also use information of your own. **(16 marks)**

How confident do you feel about each of these **skills**? Colour in the bars.

1 How do I identify change?

2 How do I evaluate whether something is a turning point?

3 How can I evaluate the extent of change?

8 Making a judgement

This unit will help you to reach a judgement, which is justified fully, in answers about change and continuity. The skills you will build are to:

- organise the information in an essay plan to help reach a judgement
- use conflicting evidence to help modify a judgement
- weight the arguments in an essay to help make a valid judgement.

In the exam, the 'how far do you agree' question requires you to make a judgement supported by criteria (reasons) that you have built up throughout your essay. This unit will help you to plan and write your own response to this type of question.

Exam-style question

'Technology was the most important factor in improving the effectiveness of policing during the nineteenth and twentieth centuries.'

How far do you agree? Explain your answer.

You may use the following in your answer:

- Metropolitan Police Force 1829
- police computers

You **must** also use information of your own. **(16 marks)**

Exam-style question

'Attitudes in society were the main reason why approaches to punishment changed in the period c1700–c1900.'

How far do you agree? Explain your answer.

You may use the following in your answer:

- the Bloody Code
- Pentonville Prison

You **must** also use information of your own. **(16 marks)**

The three key questions in the **skills boosts** will help you to plan and write a judgement.

How do I organise information to reach a judgement?

How do I deal with conflicting evidence?

How do I make a convincing judgement?

Get started

Before you can make a judgement, you need to identify what you are being asked to make a judgement on. In the 'how far' question, you could be asked to make a judgement on:

A the nature or extent of change: what types of change occurred or how much change there was

B patterns of change: the significance of a turning point

C the process of change: the causes of change or factors affecting the pace of change

D the impact of change: the consequences of a change

1 Study the exam-style questions a–d below. Which type of judgement are you being asked to make in each one? Write A, B, C or D.

a **Exam-style question**

'The introduction of the new crime of vagabondage was a turning point in the definition of criminal activity in the period c1500–c1700.'

b **Exam-style question**

'There was huge change in the definition of criminal activity in the period c1500–c1700.'

c **Exam-style question**

'Technology was the most important factor in improving the effectiveness of policing during the nineteenth and twentieth centuries.'

d **Exam-style question**

'Attitudes in society were the main reason why approaches to punishment changed in the period c1700–c1900.'

Although this is not an essential feature, you could write an introduction to show that you understand what you are being asked to make a judgement on. If you do, in a 'how far' essay it should:

- be a couple of lines long
- set out what the argument is going to be
- focus on the correct type of judgement about change (A, B, C or D).

2 Below are some answers to the exam-style question c above. Tick the answer that does all three things listed in the bullet points above.

Technology provided tools to improve the detection of crime, but government support and community involvement were also important factors.

Technology was very different at the start and end of the period. Police could catch criminals while on the beat at the start and were using mass surveillance technology at the end.

A turning point in policing was the development of speed cameras, because they could be used on a large scale and had a big impact on convictions for driving offences.

Approaches to policing, c1800–c2000, and to punishment, c1700–c1900

This unit uses the theme of approaches to policing, c1800–c2000, and to punishment, c1700–c1900, to build your skills in making a judgement. If you need to review your knowledge of this theme, work through these pages.

1. Below is a list of facts about the changing approaches to punishment. Write each one into the timeline at the correct date.

- The number of crimes in the Bloody Code reaches its highest point at 222.
- Transportation to Australia begins.
- The Death Act reduces the number of crimes carrying the death penalty to 60.
- The government ends the use of transportation and public executions.
- John Howard publishes *The State of Prisons in England and Wales*, helping to bring about prison reform.
- Pentonville Prison is built, following the principles of the separate system.
- The Prisons Act ensures that prisoners live in harsh conditions and do hard labour.

The number of crimes on the Bloody Code rises to 160.	1765	
	1777	
	1787	
	1810	
Elizabeth Fry sets up the Association for the Reformation of Female Prisoners at Newgate.	1817	
	1832	
	1842	
	1865	
	1868	
	1877	*The government takes over control of all prisons.*

2 Draw lines to link the developments in policing to their consequences.

A 1829: The Metropolitan Police Act establishes an official police force in London.

B 1856: The Police Act forces all areas to have a professional police force.

C 1878: The Criminal Investigation Department is set up with 200 detectives.

D 1901: The National Fingerprint System is set up to keep records of everyone who is arrested.

E 1946: The Fraud Squad is established to detect crimes in business and the stock market.

F 1982: The first Neighbourhood Watch scheme is launched.

G 1995: The National Automatic Fingerprint Identification System and National DNA Database are set up.

a Crimes where DNA traces or fingerprints are left behind can now be followed up more quickly.

b Detection of crimes by repeat offenders is now easier if they left fingerprint marks.

c The idea of active citizenship becomes popular, with the public helping the police by being vigilant.

d The police now have teams that specialise in certain crimes, improving their effectiveness.

e Policing priorities put increased emphasis on the detection of crime.

f Law enforcement methods are more consistent across the country.

g A police force is now under central government control.

3 Sort each of these statements, deciding whether they relate to John Howard (JH), Robert Peel (RP) or Elizabeth Fry (EF). Some may relate to more than one person.

Statement	JH	RP	EF
They campaigned to ensure prisoners were released when they finished their sentences.			
They reduced the number of capital offences by 100 in 1825.			
They visited gaolers to persuade them to improve prison conditions and practices.			
They led Bible classes and taught sewing at Newgate Prison.			
They passed a law to ensure that gaolers were paid, so they did not exploit prisoners.			
They tried to improve conditions at Newgate Prison.			

4 Complete the text about changing views on the purpose of punishment between c1700 and c1900. Use the words in the box. Not all the words are needed and some are used twice.

humanitarian retribution hard unique execution shaming separate Enlightenment Bloody

In the 18th century, the purpose of punishment was ...., in order to deter others from committing crime. The .... Code, which contained all the crimes that were punishable by death, grew, and the use of transportation, which involved an awful journey, increased. As a result, punishments involved public spectacle, like ...., or inhumane treatment, like transportation to Australia.

In the 19th century, ... concerns over execution and transportation meant that more criminals were sent to prison. At first, conditions were tough. Some prisons used the .... system, which was designed to isolate prisoners. By 1865, the emphasis was on .... labour, making prison life even more difficult. However, by c1902, the purpose of prisons shifted towards rehabilitation and the use of .... labour was coming to an end.

How do I organise information to reach a judgement?

For a 'how far' question, you need to organise the information in your response into points for and against the judgement in the question.

Exam-style question

'Technology was the most important factor in improving the effectiveness of policing during the nineteenth and twentieth centuries.'

How far do you agree? Explain your answer.

You may use the following in your answer:

- Metropolitan Police Force 1829
- police computers

You **must** also use information of your own. **(16 marks)**

1. Underline the topic focus, circle the timeframe and highlight the judgement given in the exam-style question above.
2. Identify specific aspects of the topic in the exam-style question by filling in the second column of the table below.

You can use different aspects of the topic and/or explore the aspect referred to in the judgement in different ways.

Generic factor	Specific aspect(s) of topic in the question	✓ / ✗
Individuals		
Institutions		
Science		
Technology	*Technology used for crime detection*	✓
Attitudes in society		

3. Complete the third column of the table above to show whether information related to this aspect could be used to support the argument for ✓ or against ✗ the judgement in the exam-style question.
4. Use the specific aspects you've identified to generate points for a plan using the table below. For each aspect of the topic, ask yourself 'how does this support or challenge the statement in the question?'

Specific aspect	How does this support or challenge the statement in the question?	Order
Detection technology	*Technology helped to improve the methods of crime detection.*	1

5. Order the points you've made into an outline essay plan using the third column of the table above, numbering them so that points for are first and points against are last.

2 How do I deal with conflicting evidence?

Some pieces of evidence that you use will conflict with one another, but if you can explain what this conflict reveals it can strengthen your answer.

Exam-style question

'Technology was the most important factor in improving the effectiveness of policing during the nineteenth and twentieth centuries.'

How far do you agree? Explain your answer.

You may use the following in your answer:

- Metropolitan Police Force 1829
- police computers

You **must** also use information of your own. **(16 marks)**

1. Look at some conflicting ideas two students identified when thinking about the most important factor in improving detection of crime. Identify one of your own on line C.

A Was it technology or the science behind it that improved the detection of crime?

B Was it the government's work in strengthening the police force or public support for them that made policing more effective?

C Was it .... or .... that ....?

2. This page will explore conflict A. In the table below, write one piece of evidence for each side of the argument. Then explain how the evidence answers the question.

Point	It was **technology** that led to improved detection of crime by the police.	It was developments in **forensic science** that improved the detection of crime by the police.
Evidence		
Explanation		
Weight		

3. Consider the *weight* of each of these ideas. If you think one made a bigger contribution to the topic than the other, write a + symbol under it. If you think their contribution to the topic was equal, write an = symbol underneath both.

4. Write down what the conflict reveals. In an essay, this would be a part of your link back to the question at the end of your second explanation.

A link should reinforce how the point explained in a paragraph relates to the question.

- If you wrote a + symbol underneath one idea, then explain how one needed the other to be significant.
- If you wrote an = symbol underneath both, then explain how one helped the other to be significant.

....

....

....

How do I make a convincing judgement?

There is no such thing as a 'right' judgement. In a well-written essay, you will give a judgement showing that you have weighed up the arguments to reach a decision. The process of reaching a convincing judgement is shown in the flow chart below.

Create a plan with points for and against. → Apply weight to each point, to reflect how convincing it is. → Reach a judgement, making clear what criteria you used to weight the arguments.

Exam-style question

'Technology was the most important factor in improving the effectiveness of policing during the nineteenth and twentieth centuries.'

How far do you agree? Explain your answer

You may use the following in your answer:

- Metropolitan Police Force 1829
- police computers

You **must** also use information of your own. **(16 marks)**

① Add a point for and against to the plan below. Your point against should relate to another factor.

A *For: Technology improved the effectiveness of police in identifying criminals.*

B *For:* ....

C *Against: Robert Peel set up the first official police force.*

D *Against:* ....

② Consider each point in ① and write a score reflecting how convincing you find it: up to 5 if the point strengthens the argument in support of the statement in the question, and down to –5 if it weakens it.

③ Explain the weighting for one of your points, making your criteria clear. A student answer, which could be used as part of a conclusion, is provided for the first argument.

Consider the following:

- How many people were affected?
- How important was it in helping other developments to occur?
- How reliant was it on other developments?
- How big an impact did it have on the topic focus in the judgement?

To remind yourself of criteria to help you assess, see Unit 7.

Argument	How much weight did you give it? (out of 5)	Explain your decision, referring to the statement in the question and the criteria in ②.
A	+4	*Technology had a big impact on the identification of criminals using fingerprints, blood and DNA samples. However, its importance is limited because it only influenced the later part of the timeframe.*

Sample response

A good conclusion is an important feature of a 'how far' essay. Comparing a strong student answer with a weaker one will help you when writing your own.

Exam-style question

'The role of government was the most important factor in changing approaches to policing during the nineteenth and twentieth centuries.'

How far do you agree? Explain your answer.

You may use the following in your answer:

- development of the Metropolitan Police Force
- specialisation

You **must** also use information of your own. **(16 marks)**

Study the plan below before examining the student answers in (1).

Point 1: The government created legislation to set up a national system of police forces.
Point 2: The government encouraged the specialisation of the police force.
Point 3: However, new technologies allowed the police to catch criminals in different ways.
Point 4: The support of the public also meant the police could involve them in policing.

(1) Annotate the strong and weak student conclusions below. Here are some features to look for:

Features of a strong conclusion	Features of a weak conclusion
A Use of criteria to support judgements **B** Direct comparison of factors **C** References to the argument for and against	**D** Unsupported assertion: a judgement without criteria to support it **E** Repetition of points from the essay **F** The use of new evidence

Strong student response:

The most important factor in changing approaches to policing was the support from the government in setting up police forces, such as the Metropolitan Police, because without their legislation and funding, the first police force could not have been set up and used as a template for other police forces. Their support was more important than new technology, because even though the development of speed cameras and CCTV helped the police to catch criminals, the police still needed government funding, as well as legal support for the deployment of these technologies, to use them. However, the police could only change their approach if they had the means to do so, which is why developments in computing technology were important, as they enabled the police to catch criminals more efficiently and more often. They also relied on public support, through programmes like Neighbourhood Watch, to improve the effectiveness of their focus on the prevention of crime. Even so, without government support, changing the roles of the police and supporting their work, policing would not have changed as much, because the government provided the basis for later changes and the funding to make them possible.

Weak student response:

The government was the most important reason, because they were important to changing what the police did. However, there were other reasons, like advances in technology and changes in public attitudes. For example, mass video surveillance allowed the police to focus on the detection of terrorist activities. This was created by inventors and scientists, who were also important.

Your turn!

Now it's your turn to try to answer an exam-style question.

Exam-style question

'Technology was the most important factor in improving the effectiveness of policing during the nineteenth and twentieth centuries.'

How far do you agree? Explain your answer.

You may use the following in your answer:

- the Bloody Code
- Pentonville Prison

You **must** also use information of your own. **(16 marks)**

1 Write an essay plan, covering three to four points. The first one or two points must agree with the judgement in the exam-style question and the rest disagree, exploring alternative reasons.

Point 1:

Point 2:

Point 3:

Point 4:

2 a Highlight two conflicting points in your plan and explain on a separate piece of paper what the conflict reveals.

b If you think one of your highlighted points made a bigger contribution to the topic than the other, put a tick next to it.

c If you think their contribution to the topic was equal, place an = symbol next to them both.

3 Weight the points in your plan from -5 to $+5$, reflecting how convincing you find each of them.

4 Write a conclusion, making clear the criteria (reasons) for your judgement.

Review your skills

Check up

Review your response to the exam-style question on page 79. Tick the column to show how well you think you have done each of the following.

	Had a go	Nearly there	Got it!
organised the information in my plan around points for and against the judgement in the question	☐	☐	☐
used conflicting evidence to modify my judgement	☐	☐	☐
made a valid judgement, reflecting the weight I assigned to each of the arguments in my essay	☐	☐	☐

Look over all of your work in this unit. Note down three things you have learned that you will apply when making a judgement.

1. ....
2. ....
3. ....

Need more practice?

On separate paper, try the exam-style question below.

Exam-style question

'The role of government was the main reason why approaches to punishment changed in the period c1700–c1900.'

How far do you agree? Explain your answer.

You may use the following in your answer:

- transportation to Australia
- Elizabeth Fry

You **must** also use information of your own. **(16 marks)**

How confident do you feel about each of these **skills**? Colour in the bars.

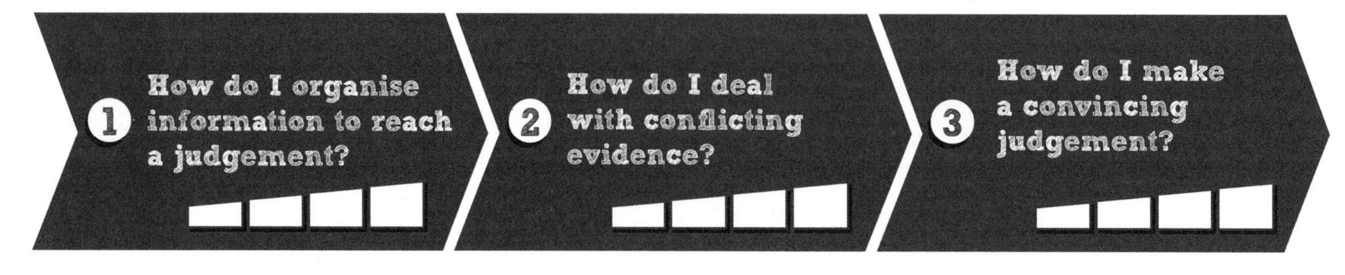

Answers

Unit 1

Page 2

1. **Cross out:** An argument about what the information suggests or proves.

2.

	Feature	Specific detail
Police officers could be attacked.	✓	
By the 1870s, the Metropolitan Police had to carry out roles defined in 82 laws.		✓
In 1888, there were an estimated 62 brothels in Whitechapel.		✓
There were a lot of violent drunks in Whitechapel.	✓	
Police only had a truncheon to protect themselves if attacked.		✓
There was a large number of prostitutes on the streets.	✓	

3. a, b, c

The streets of London were dangerous. ~~A detail that demonstrates this is that~~ there were gangs like the Bessarabian Tigers.

~~One feature of the problems facing police in Whitechapel is that~~ Alcoholism was a serious problem. Whitechapel Road had 45 places that served alcohol on it.

There was a large number of prostitutes in Whitechapel. ~~From my own knowledge I know that~~ there were 62 brothels in Whitechapel by 1888.

Page 3

1. Whitechapel was policed by members of H Division, which was a part of the Metropolitan Police Force. H Division had 500 constables, who went out on the beat around Whitechapel. On their beat, ~~constables were not allowed to talk to members of the public unless they were approached by them~~ they were supposed to stop to question people.

The police faced many difficulties, even though ~~they were popular in poor areas like Whitechapel. They supported public protests and were ordered not to stop them, improving their popularity were unpopular in poor areas like Whitechapel.~~ They put down public protests against unpopular government decisions, damaging their popularity. However, if they did get into trouble, they only had truncheons to defend themselves.

Policing was a difficult job made worse by the problems of poverty. For example, prostitution was not illegal, but sex workers were vulnerable to attack. Drunks were also a problem, ~~but it was difficult to find places to buy a drink~~ as it was easy to find places to buy a drink. Finally, gangs ran protection rackets, which the police were powerless to deal with effectively.

2. **Box 2:** Segregation was a feature of life in Whitechapel.

Box 3: Some immigrants brought revolutionary ideas with them.

Box 4: Socialists encouraged people to protest.

Page 4

3. **True:** a, c, e

False: b, d

4. **Box 2:** The Bertillon system

Box 3: Crime-scene photography

Box 4: Large-scale Jewish immigration

Box 5: Immigration from Eastern Europe

Page 5

1. **Topic focus:** the problems facing police in Whitechapel
2. A b; B a; C f; D c; E g; F e; G d
3. Student's own response, but you might write:

The police dealt with crimes involving theft.

The police did not make much use of crime-scene photography.

Page 6

1. Student's own response, but you might write:

Box 1: Negative attitudes towards the police

Box 2: Police were attacked by violent gangs like the Bessarabian Tigers; Gangs made some places no-go areas for the police, such as the slum of Ewer Street; Police working as poor relief officers were unpopular.

Box 4 (left): Unpopular role as poor relief officers

Box 4 (right): The name of a slum

2. **Specific feature:** The police faced problems caused by poverty.

Supporting detail: The residents of Whitechapel lived in rookeries where theft was common.

3. Student's own response, but might include: The police faced problems caused by negative attitudes towards them. Gangs made some places no-go areas for the police, such as the slum of Ewer Street.
4. Student's own response, but, for the example given above, could be:

Specific feature: The police faced problems caused by negative attitudes towards them.

Supporting detail: Gangs made some places no-go areas for the police, such as the slum of Ewer Street.

Page 7

1. **Feature:** threatened by new working-class political groups.

Details: anarchists, who wanted to overthrow the government; Special Branch decided to set up an operation to monitor suspected anarchists in 1893; socialists, who founded the Social Democratic Foundation in 1881; Bloody Sunday in 1887.

Explanation: they disliked the idea of the police, making them unpopular, and they were suspected terrorists, so the police had to spend time monitoring them.

2 Student's own response, but you might tick:

Do not include explanation of the feature.

Do not include more than one piece of additional detail.

3 ~~One of the problems facing police in Whitechapel was that~~ they were threatened by new working-class political groups. ~~One group was the anarchists, who wanted to overthrow the government.~~ Special Branch decided to set up an operation to monitor suspected anarchists in 1893. ~~Another group was the socialists, who founded the Social Democratic Foundation in 1881. They were involved in the events that led to Bloody Sunday in 1887. Both groups were a problem because they disliked the idea of the police, making them unpopular, and they were suspected terrorists, so the police had to spend time monitoring them.~~

4 Student's own response, but you might write: The police were threatened by new working-class political groups. One group was the socialists, who founded the Social Democratic Foundation in 1881.

Page 8

1 **Feature:** Had to deal with violence between longer-established residents and immigrants.

Detail: Large numbers of Irish immigrants settled in the East End from the 1840s onwards.

Detail: They were not well-liked by longer-established residents.

2 **Feature 1:** They could not make much use of modern technology in their investigations. For example, crime-scene photography was in its very early stages of development. ~~Cameras were used to record some evidence.~~

Feature 2: Police to deal with violence between longer-established residents and immigrants. Large numbers of Irish immigrants settled in the East End from the 1840s onwards. ~~They were not well liked by longer established residents.~~

Page 9

1 Student's own response, but could include the following:

Types of people: Members of the public

Technology: N/A

Groups: Group of vigilantes

Ideas and attitudes: Influenced media reporting

Types of crime: Murders

Policing methods used: Encouraged people to volunteer information

2 a – d Student's own response.

Unit 2

Page 12

1 **Origin:** Author/creator details

Purpose: Why a source was created

Provenance: The NOP of a source

Usefulness: What a source can be used for

Reliability: How much a source can be trusted

Criteria: A way of judging a source

2 **Tick:** A, C, D

Page 13

1 A: a, e, f

B: c, g, j

C: b, h, i

D: d, k, l

2 a Student's own response, but you might write: old, sick, disabled, orphans, single mothers and the very poor.

b Student's own response, but you might write: harsh conditions, strict discipline, tough manual labour and families were split up.

c Student's own response, but you might write: sweatshop conditions.

d Student's own response, but you might write: availability of work varied or there was a period of economic depression in the 1870s.

Page 14

3 a B; b C; c A; d A; e C

4 A b; B e ; C a; D f; E c; F d

Page 15

1 a **Source B:** From a report on sanitary conditions by Joseph Loane in 1889. Loane was a Medical Officer of Health for the Whitechapel District.

Tick: To report on the living conditions in Whitechapel

b Student's own response, but you might tick: authoritative or reliable.

2 and 3 Student's own response, but you might suggest that Source B is authoritative: The author of Source B had experience of working as a Medical Officer of Health, so is in a good position to tell us about the problems he saw. Or you could choose a criterion that possibly weakens the usefulness of the source: Source B may not be reliable because the author may have selected examples to try to convince the government to improve the conditions for the poor in Whitechapel.

Page 16

1 **Topic focus:** The extent of poverty in Whitechapel.

2 Rich people tried to help the poor. Poor people could not afford to move into new houses built for them. Poor quality housing was cleared for new housing.

3 Student's own response, but it might resemble the following: Source B is useful as it tells us about the extent of poverty in Whitechapel, because it says that poor people could not afford to move into new houses that had been built for them. This is useful because it suggests that this would put pressure on other sources of accommodation for the poor.

4 Student's own response, as they are all correct, but if you chose the inference made in the answer for 3, you might tick: 'Unable to afford their own separate homes, 8,000 people lived in 200 lodging houses in Whitechapel.'

5. Student's own response but you might write: This is an accurate suggestion, because I know that 8,000 people lived in 200 lodging houses in Whitechapel, which would have been seriously overcrowded.

Page 17

1. **Nature:** Report

   Origin: Joseph Loane, Medical Officer of Health, Whitechapel District, written in 1889

   Purpose: Unclear

2. Student's own response, but you might write:

   A It was written as a report on the sanitary conditions in Whitechapel.

   B The officer would visit the area, observe the conditions and talk to the residents.

   C/D Whitechapel suffered high levels of poverty with 30,709 people in 4,069 houses or on the street in 1881.

   E To report on the living conditions in Whitechapel.

3. Student's own response, but you might write: Source B gives an authoritative view because Loane was a Medical Officer who would have worked in Whitechapel and knew the area and its people well.

Page 18

1. Source B is useful for an enquiry about the extent of poverty in Whitechapel because it describes the problem of overcrowding. The Medical Officer says that wretched hovels were cleared, which suggests that there were plenty of them in Whitechapel. **(F)** This is accurate, as rookeries were common, and could have up to 30 people in one apartment. **(C)**

   Source B's usefulness is strengthened by the fact that it comes from a Medical Officer of Health. More authority can be given to the poverty described in this source, because he was appointed to check on public health. **(D)** This included the district of Whitechapel, where up to 1,000 people were homeless. **(A)** However, Source B may not be objective, as Loane may want to improve the conditions in Whitechapel. **(E)**

2. B. The student could have used contextual knowledge, like the development of the Peabody Estate in 1881, to explain that Loane might be trying to encourage more actions like this.

Page 19

1. Student's own response, but you might write:

   What is the topic focus of the enquiry? The extent of poverty in Whitechapel

   What can you learn from the content of the source? The streets were overcrowded.

   What do you know that supports or challenges the accuracy of the contents? There were around 1,000 homeless people out of a population of 30,000 in Whitechapel.

   What does the source tell you about its provenance? Nature: Sketch

   Origin: Gustav Doré, a Frenchman who toured London and visited Whitechapel, 1872. Produced in private.

   Purpose: To illustrate a book about a tour of London.

   What do you know about the provenance from your contextual knowledge? Source: sketches can exaggerate an issue to make a point.

   Place: Whitechapel suffered from serious problems of poverty.

   Time: It is before any major slum clearance programmes had begun.

   How does this affect the strength of the source for the enquiry (refer to criteria)? It makes it more authoritative in its description of the extent of poverty in Whitechapel, as the artist is aiming to describe rather than promote change.

2. Student's own response.

Unit 3

Page 22

1. Student's own response, but you might write:

Generic type of source	Specific type of source
Diary	Diary of an inmate at a workhouse
Records	Records of the Central Criminal Court
Statistics	Government statistics of the numbers of crimes committed in Whitechapel
Reports	A report from a police officer from Metropolitan Police H Division
Newspaper	An *Illustrated London News* article about the events of Bloody Sunday
Census	The accounts of a workhouse in Whitechapel

2. A b; B a; C c; D e; E d

Page 23

1. A c; B e; C d; D b; E a

2. **A Beat constable:** He was supposed to stop to question people; He could act as a poor relief officer, taking people to the workhouse.

   B Police commissioner: Sir Charles Warren, a former general, was appointed to this position in 1886; He used the army to stop the protest in Trafalgar Square on Bloody Sunday.

   C Home Secretary: He had little control over police forces outside of London; He controlled the Metropolitan Police Force, appointing its commissioner.

3. **a** B

   b B

Page 24

4. **a** A

   b C

   c C

5. Superintendent of a division 3; Metropolitan Police Commissioner 2; Home Secretary 1; Sergeant 4; Constable 5

6. Students should add in this order: Metropolitan; low; restrict; protest; gangs; Whitechapel; workhouses; poverty.

Page 25

1. The effectiveness of policing
2. Student's own response, but you might write the annotations below.

   Police have their back turned to criminals.

   It says there are not many police officers.

   Statements say there is a low ratio of police officers to people.
3. Student's own response.
4. a. Student's own response, but you might write:

   Chosen detail: Members of the criminal class saying it's lucky there are so few police officers.

   How it relates to the topic: It relates to how well staffed the police were.

   b. Student's own response, but you might write: A journalist might have written an article about police staffing levels and the effect this had on tackling crime.

Page 26

1. a. **Topic:** the effectiveness of policing

   b. There are three possible correct answers, but you only need to choose one. You could use: The police officer has his back turned to the criminals; The criminals say there are not many police officers; The commissioner says they do not have large reserves of police officers doing nothing.
2. Possible questions depend on which detail is chosen in 1; see ideas below.

Detail in Source A that I would follow up	Question I would ask
The criminals say there are not many police officers.	Was there a connection between police staffing levels and the number of crimes?
The commissioner says they do not have large reserves of police officers doing nothing.	Why were there staffing problems in the Metropolitan Police?

3. Student's own response.
4. Student's own response, but you might write:

   Detail in Source A that I would follow up: The low police to public ratio.

   Question I would ask: What problems did the police experience due to their lack of numbers?

Page 27

1. Student's own response, but you might write:

   Diaries from residents of London who had witnessed or been a victim of crime.

   Interviews by journalists of members of the public about police visibility and its impact on crime.

   Police reports on crimes that officers had been unable to prevent.
2. Student's own response.
3. Student's own response, but you might write:

   Interviews by journalists of members of the public. They could provide more details of the public view, as portrayed by journalists, of the adequacy of police staffing numbers.

   Police reports on crimes that officers had been unable to prevent. They might confirm whether police officers thought that staffing problems improved a criminal's chance of success.

Page 28

1. **Tick:** Has the student chosen a detail that relates to the topic in the exam-style question?
2. **Tick:** How did the police manage to catch so many criminals?
3. Student's own response, but you might write: Police records on the number of arrests compared to the amount of crime reported.

Page 29

1. Student's own response, but you might write:

1 What is the topic in the question?	The workings of the Metropolitan Police.	
2 List two to three details in the source that relate to the topic. 3 Highlight one detail that could lead to an enquiry about the topic and which there are likely to be other sources about.	'Most of the criminals are caught by the ordinary police.' It is surprising that 'cases of burglary… are not twenty times higher'. The police have to watch over 'immense districts of houses'.	
4 Frame a question that relates to your selected detail, is about an aspect of the topic in the exam-style question and that an historian could answer.	How were the Metropolitan Police able to catch so many criminals?	
5 Choose a specific type of source that could provide more details to answer your planned question, place your selected detail in context or confirm the accuracy of the supplied source.	A police handbook given to new recruits about the role and work of a constable.	
6 Tick which of these your chosen type of source helps with.	It provides more details to answer your planned question.	✓
	It places your selected detail in context.	
	It confirms that the detail you have selected gives an accurate impression of the situation.	

2. Student's own response, but another way you could write up the question is:

   Detail in Source B that I would follow up: 'Most of the criminals are caught by the ordinary police.'

   Question I would ask: How effective were the police in catching criminals?

What type of source I could use: Home Office crime statistics, showing the number of criminals caught.

How this might help answer my question: It might reveal whether constables really did catch a lot of criminals in the Metropolitan Police Force area, or whether this is just the impression the journalist wanted to give.

Unit 4

Page 32

1. A Explains

   B Describes

2. but

3. Student's own response, but you might make the following rewrites:

   A The hue and cry was raised to catch criminals in the medieval period. *This practice continued* by using the hue and cry in the 16th century.

   B Men helped to catch criminals in medieval times *and they were* required to act as constables in the 16th century, with some powers to arrest suspects.

   C Volunteer night watchmen patrolled towns at night in the 16th century. *However*, Robert Peel set up a professional police force in the 19th century.

   D Coroners were appointed in the 12th century to investigate suspicious deaths *and still* investigate them in the 21st century.

   E The police began to keep national crime records in the 19th century and *this practice remained with* the Police National Computer in the 1980s.

   F Professional thief-takers were paid a fee to catch criminals in the 17th century, *but* in the next century some worked for the Bow Street Runners, which the government began to fund in 1785.

Page 33

1. **c1000:** Witnesses of a crime raise a hue and cry to catch criminals.

   1361: Edward III appoints Justices of the Peace to act as magistrates and enforce the law.

   c1500: Town constables and night watchmen become more common figures in towns.

   1690: Mounted customs officers are introduced to try and catch smugglers.

   1748: Henry Fielding establishes the Bow Street Runners, using 'Principal Officers' to catch criminals.

   1829: The Metropolitan Police Act provides London with a uniformed police force.

   1856: The County and Borough Police Act forces all areas to have a police force funded and inspected by the central government.

   c1920s: Women are allowed to become police officers and begin to join police forces.

   c1970s and 80s: The Police National Computer is set up, centralising the records used by the police.

   1982: The first Neighbourhood Watch scheme is established, encouraging local residents to be vigilant.

Page 34

2. A c; B d; C a; D b

3. **1000–1500** Local officials are renamed constables instead of tithingmen; Coroners are appointed to investigate suspicious deaths; Local law enforcers report to the shire reeve.

   1500–1700 Hue and cry continues to be used, alongside newer practices; Town constables are employed by the town authorities.

   1700–1900 Soldiers are used to deal with riots; Special Branch is set up to investigate terrorists.

   1900–present Technology such as speed cameras is used to enforce the law; Police bicycles and cars are used to catch criminals.

4. a **Tithingman:** One man who represents his tithing group in law enforcement.

   b **Hue and cry:** A shout for help to catch criminals.

   c **Customs officer:** An official who tries to track down smugglers.

   d **Principal officer:** A thief-taker appointed by Fielding to the Bow Street Runners.

   e **Detective:** Someone who investigates crime in plain clothes.

Page 35

1. a explain

   b difference

2. Number of features: 1; number of marks: 4

3. a **Topic focus:** the role of local communities in law enforcement

   b **Timeframes:** the medieval period (c1000–c1500) and 19th century

4. The stronger student is Student A, because they focus on law enforcement, give detail from the correct timeframes and offer an explanation.

Page 36

1. **Concept (circle):** Difference

   Topic: The role of local communities in law enforcement

   Timeframe 1: Medieval period (c1000–c1500)

   Timeframe 2: 19th century

2. **Tick:** methods used to catch criminals; way crime was reported

   Student's own response but could include: government role, extent of professionalisation, roles in law enforcement.

3. Student's own response, depending on the answer chosen from 2, but you might write:

   Choice: Methods used to catch criminals

   Medieval law enforcement: The hue and cry system involved shouting for help, so that everyone who heard could help chase and capture suspects.

   19th-century law enforcement: Police constables blew a whistle or used a rattle to alert other police officers to help them catch a criminal.

4. Student's own response, but you might write: Criminals could be arrested by professional police officers.

Page 37

1, 2 and 3 Student's own response, but you might write:

One way in which the role of local communities in law enforcement was different was the nature of a person's involvement.

In the medieval period, members of a tithing had to find and catch criminals from their group.

In the 20th century, members of a local community could join a Neighbourhood Watch scheme voluntarily.

This shows that the involvement of the local community shifted from a compulsory to a voluntary role.

Page 38

1. **Student 1 (strong):** One similarity between the 16th and 18th centuries was the jobs available in law enforcement **(A)**. In the 16th century, night watchmen patrolled the streets at night on a voluntary basis **(B)**. In the 18th century, householders still acted as part-time watchmen and constables **(C)**. This shows that householders maintained an important role in law enforcement in towns **(D)**.
2. **Student 2 (weak):** One similarity between the 16th and 18th centuries was the extent of crime linked to towns **(A)**. In the medieval period, towns had become a popular target for thieves because they were centres for trade **(B)**. In the 16th century, the crime of vagabondage was introduced and targeted the poor who wandered into towns **(C)**. It was punished harshly under the Vagrancy Act of 1547 and the 1597 Act for the Relief of the Poor **(D)**. In the 18th century, another crime was caused by travel between towns **(C)**. Highway robbery became more common, as people transported their goods and money between towns **(D)**. To punish it, the death penalty was introduced in 1772 **(D)**. The problems remained the same, because towns were important places **(E)**.

Page 39

1. Student's own response, but you might write:

   Concept (circle): Difference

   Topic: Law enforcement in towns

   Timeframe 1: 16th century

   Timeframe 2: 19th century

2. Student's own response, but you might write:

   One way in which law enforcement in towns was different was how much control the central government had over it.

   In the 16th century, town authorities appointed their town constable.

   In the 19th century, the Police Act established police forces that were inspected and funded by central government.

   This shows that the power of central government over law enforcement had increased, as central government was involved more closely with the organisation of law enforcement and its operations.

Unit 5

Page 42

1. A b; B e; C d; D g; E f; F c; G a
2. Student's own response, but you might write:

   A date: 1542, 1645, 1647, 1735 and 1736

   An individual or group: Henry VIII, Elizabeth I, James I and Matthew Hopkins

   A named development: The Witchcraft Act of 1735

   A statistic: 1,000 people executed.

3. Student's own response, but you might write:

   One reason the number of accusations of witchcraft changed quickly was that monarchs supported accusations. ~~One king had started the process in the 16th century~~ **(1)**. ~~Another had made a law that applied to even more people~~ **(2)**. This led to rapid change because people could now make accusations against witches that the authorities would investigate.

   (1) Henry VIII had passed a law against witchcraft in 1542.

   (2) James I followed this up with a law against conjuring in 1604.

Page 43

1. A a; B b; C b; D a
2. The changes were gradual because it took a long time for attitudes to change, especially because alternative approaches had to be thought of and it cost money to implement the changes.
3. a False. After 1563, witches were tried in the common court.

   b False. They were often made by wealthy individuals against poor individuals.

   c True.

   d False. He operated in East Anglia.

   e True.

   f False. There were less accusations

Page 44

4. a H; b W; c W; d H; e W; f W; g H; h W; i H; j H
5. A 8; B 6; C 7; D 9; E 4; F 5; G 3; H 10; I 1; J 2

Page 45

1. **Topic focus:** the use of the death penalty

   Timeframe: c1900 to the present day

2. Student's own response, but you might write:

   Attitudes: The attitude towards young offenders

   Institutions: The role of the government

3. Specific information:

   The attitude towards young offenders:

   - The 1908 Children's Act ended the hanging of under-16s.
   - The Prevention of Crime Act created a national system of borstals in 1908.
   - Alexander Patterson, a prisons commissioner, changed how young offenders were treated between 1922 and 1947.

   The role of the government:

   - The government passed a law restricting the death penalty to capital murders in 1957.
   - The Home Secretary in 1965, Roy Jenkins, wanted to end the death penalty.
   - The British government signed the 6th protocol of the European Convention on Human Rights in 1999.

4. Student's own response.

Page 46

1. Student's own response, but to get a good spread across the timeframe you might suggest:

   Individuals: A – 5,000 people protested on the night of Derek Bentley's execution in 1953.

   Attitudes: B – Young offenders were no longer subject to the death penalty when the hanging of under-18s ended in 1933.

   Institutions: E – The British government agreed to the 6th protocol of the European Convention on Human Rights in 1999.

2. a why

   b Why a change occurred

3. Answer 3

4. Student's own response, but you might write:

   A: This encouraged the government to reduce the use of the death penalty.

   E: This meant the death penalty could no longer be used in Britain.

Page 47

1. **Topic focus:** the use of the death penalty

   Timeframe: c1900 to the present day

2. and 3. Student's own response, but you might write:

   Individuals: The Derek Bentley case

   Institutions: The Royal Commission on Capital Punishment

   Science: Advances in forensic science

   Attitudes in society: Attitudes towards young offenders

4. Student's own response, but you might write:

   Advances in forensic science: Developments in DNA testing allowed for greater accuracy in catching criminals

5. Student's own response, but you might suggest:

   Cause (Point): People began to see young offenders differently to other criminals.

   Information (Evidence): Young offenders were put into separate prisons, called borstals, after the first borstal was set up in 1902.

   Cause (Point): Advances in forensic science helped challenge some cases where the accused had been executed.

   Information (Evidence): The execution of Timothy Evans (1950) was found to be a miscarriage of justice, partly as a result of forensic analysis of new evidence.

Page 48

1. a **Strong student answer:**

   Underline: 1645, Matthew Hopkins was employed by a JP

   Double underline: change occurred quickly because Hopkins was motivated

   b **Weak student answer:**

   Underline: witches in England, using local gossip,

   Double underline: shows that there were a lot of ways to catch witches; caused the number of accusations to change quickly.

   c Student A's answer is stronger as it offers precise information and the concept in the question is clearly focused on.

Page 49

1. a – c Student's own response, but you might write:

   Individuals: The work of Matthew Hopkins

   Institutions: New government legislation

   Attitudes in society: Changes in religion

   d **Tick:** Why there was rapid/quick change

2. Student's own response but you might write:

   Cause (Point): Matthew Hopkins encouraged a witch hunt in East Anglia.

   Information (Evidence): Matthew Hopkins' actions led to around 300 individuals being investigated for witchcraft.

   Cause (Point): The government passed laws making it possible to accuse people of witchcraft.

   Information (Evidence): James I's government passed the Witchcraft and Conjuration Act, making the act of summoning evil spirits punishable by death.

   Cause (Point): Changes in religion created a fear of magic.

   Information (Evidence): Henry VIII broke away from the Catholic Church in 1534.

Unit 6

Page 52

1. A c; B d; C a; D b

2. a C; b A; c B; d D; e E

Page 53

1. **Trial by ordeal:** A, C, E, J

   Trial by combat: D, G, I, K

   Judgement by community: B, F, H, L

2. A c; B a; C b; D d

Page 54

3. **Missing words:** rich; tithe; penance; moral; benefit; sanctuary.

4. a Members of the tithing group; b King's shire reeve; c A priest; d Local lord; e The bishop

5. **True:** a, c

   False: b, d, e

Page 55

1. **Topic focus:** influence of the Church on law enforcement

   Process of change: changed slowly

2. Student's own response but you might write:

   B: The Church could judge criminals;

   C: The Church judged criminals who were clerics.

3. (Based on suggested answers in 2):

   b Explain why there was slow change in the power of the Church to judge criminals.

   c Explain why there was slow change in the power of the Church to judge criminals who were clerics.

4 b and c Student's own response, but based on the questions suggested above you might write: the authorities relied on the Church to judge some criminals; the Church protected its own power.

5 Some kings gave the Church control over aspects of law enforcement.

Page 56

1 Student's own response, but you might write: Medieval people believed in sin.

2 **Highlight:** the authorities relied on the Church to administer the trial

3 Student's own response, but you might write: Another reason the influence of the Church on law enforcement changed slowly was that the Church influenced people's views. It promoted the view that crime was sinful.

4 a–c One reason the influence of the Church changed slowly was that the authorities sometimes relied on it. For example, Anglo-Saxon justice relied on an oath made to God by the accused to swear their innocence. If they lied, the Church taught they would be punished by God. This meant an important way that people received justice, by swearing an oath of innocence, was backed up by Church teaching.

5 Student's own response.

Page 57

1 a **Topic and concept focus:** slow change in the influence of the Church on law enforcement

b **Reason in answer to the question:** the Church protected its own power

c **Own knowledge:** The Church had the power to judge criminals who were also clerics. When Henry II tried to take this power away in the 1160s, the Church resisted him.

d **Explanation of how own knowledge proves point:** This meant it kept the power of 'benefit of clergy'.

2 **Link:** This led to slow change in the Church's influence on law enforcement, because the king struggled to take power away from it.

3 Student's own response, but you might write: until other methods of testing the accused were developed, the Church kept its influence on a traditional method that was widely accepted.

4 Student's own response, but you might write: the Church could use its power to protect its position.

Page 58

1 **Point:** yellow; **Knowledge:** blue; **Explanation:** pink; **Link back to the question:** Green

2 The Church had its own courts.

3 It helps to build up your overall argument.

Page 59

1 Student's own response but you could include the following:

Point: One reason why the Church's influence changed slowly was that some kings supported it.

Supporting knowledge: William I encouraged the Church to set up courts to deal with moral crimes.

Explanation: As a result, the Church could rule on sinful behaviours in another way.

Link back to the question: The effect of this was slow change, because it increased the Church's established power in controlling behaviour.

2 and 3 Student's own responses.

Unit 7

Page 62

1 **Tick:** To open a paragraph, focusing on one aspect of the question; To support or illustrate your point with precisely selected information; To explain how your information proves the point you are making; To build up your overall argument in relation to the question set.

2 a **Point:** There was a huge change in the government's attitude towards crime.

b **Evidence:** England's population was growing, which resulted in a fall in wages and a rise in the cost of living.

c **Explanation:** This meant that there were more homeless people without a job moving from place to place, which the government saw as a threat. So the government made vagrancy a serious crime in 1547.

d **Link:** This led to a huge change in the definition of criminal activity, because the nationwide problem of vagrancy meant that the government saw it as a threat and turned it into a crime in both urban and rural communities.

3 The student's answer should label and identify the following:

Scale of change: nationwide problem; in both rural and urban communities

Measurements of extent: huge change; huge change

Page 63

1 a A b A c B d C e B

2 a The association of treason with heresy meant that more people were punished severely for refusing to follow the official teaching of the Church of England.

b The Vagrancy Act of 1547 was not significant in the short term because it was withdrawn after three years.

c The Game Act meant that crimes related to poverty were treated more seriously by the authorities.

d The extension of the definition of witchcraft was significant because it meant more people were turned into criminals by the law.

Page 64

3 A d; B a; C c; D b; E f; F e

4 a The first open prison was established in 1933 to ~~punish criminals severely~~ help reintegrate criminals.

b During the Second World War, conscientious objectors were treated ~~harshly~~ with respect by the authorities.

c Alexander Patterson, a prisons commissioner, campaigned for ~~restorative~~ justice reform.

d In 1965, the Home Secretary, Roy Jenkins, ended ~~transportation~~ the death penalty.

e To monitor convicts outside of prison, ~~mobile phones~~ electronic tags were used to track them.

f Anti-Social Behaviour Orders were introduced to ~~force criminals to do hard labour~~ place restrictions on criminals.

Page 65

1. **Topic focus:** the methods used to punish criminals

   Timeframe: c1800 to the present day

2. At the start of the period, methods used to punish criminals included the death penalty and public executions, transportation to Australia and incarceration in prisons with poor living conditions.

   At the end of the period, methods used to punish criminals no longer included the death penalty and were more varied, including a prison system that prepared prisoners for life outside prison and a range of punishments outside of the prison environment, such as community service and electronic tagging.

3. Student's own response, but might include any four of:

   Roy Jenkins' opposition to the death penalty; The government brought all prisons under their authority, 1877; Electronic tagging; Public executions were viewed as too much of a fun spectacle

4. Student's own response, but might include:

   Henry VIII's break with Rome, 1534; The Gunpowder Plot, 1605; Oliver Cromwell's Puritan rule, 1650s; The strengthening of the Church of England, 1534 onwards; Introduction of customs duties; Fear of witchcraft

Page 66

1. **Topic focus:** the methods used to punish criminals

   Timeframe: c1800 to the present day

   Turning point: The end of transportation

2. **A:** Convicts had to be punished in Britain; **B:** Prisons became central to the system of punishment; **C:** Criminals could still be sentenced to death.

3. Student's own response, but might include:

Did it affect the pace of change?	
Evidence that the pace of change sped up	**Evidence that the pace of change slowed down or stayed the same**
The pace of change in the development of prisons sped up.	Prisons were still used as places of punishment, so the treatment of convicts remained harsh.
Did it break with a trend?	
Evidence that it was a major disruption in a trend	**Evidence that it was part of a trend of similar changes (list other events/developments that affected the topic in the question)**
It broke with a trend in relying on transportation to deter criminals.	It was a part of a trend in the increased use of prisons.

Did it lead to a significant amount of change?	
Evidence that it led to significant change	**Evidence that other turning points were more significant**
It led to a significant increase in the use of prisons.	The abolition of the death penalty and the reform of youth justice were also significant turning points.

4. Student's own response, but might include:

   An argument that the end of transportation was a turning point was that it increased the speed of change in the development of prisons as the main form of punishment.

   However, it may not have been a turning point, as the use of the death penalty continued as an important method of punishment.

Page 67

1. **Topic focus:** the definition of criminal activity

   Timeframe: c1500–c1700

2. **State of affairs c1500:** Vagabondage was treated as a social problem and people were sent back to their place of birth; Witchcraft was dealt with by the Church; Heresy was a serious crime and heretics could be burnt at the stake.

3. **a** **What was the scale of the change?** National: the definitions of crimes changed across England.

   b **How much change was there in people's attitudes and the role of institutions?** Significant change: in the activities people defined as criminal, but less so in the role of authorities. The authorities already had power to prevent individuals' actions challenging authority before 1500.

   c **How much continuity was there between the start and end of the period?** A lot stayed the same: there was continuity in crimes like theft, challenging authority and causing physical harm.

4. Student's own response, based on the answers to 3.

Page 68

1. The new crime of vagabondage led to significant change, as poverty was now seen as a serious crime rather than a social problem. Before the mid-16th century, vagabondage had been treated as a social problem, which the community that the poor person came from would have to deal with. During the Tudor period, new legislation, like the Vagrancy Act of 1547, distinguished between the deserving poor and sturdy beggars. This meant some forms of poverty were clearly defined as criminal. This makes the new crime of vagabondage a turning point because the government turned a method of survival for the able-bodied poor into a criminal activity for which increasingly harsh punishments were given.

   However, the new crime of vagabondage was also part of a trend in widening the definition of what the state considered to be a crime. In the 16th century, new laws were passed to make witchcraft illegal, such as the 1542 Witchcraft Act. This continued in the 17th century, when James I widened the definition of practices associated with witchcraft. Both of these developments meant that the state was defining crimes to control people's behaviour and did so throughout the period.

This suggests the new crime of vagabondage was less of a turning point, because it was part of a trend towards criminalising certain behaviours.

② Students should tick all three rows of the checklist.

Page 69

① Student's own response, but might include:

1 It broke with a trend in relying on the death penalty for the most serious crimes.

2 It was a significant change as the emphasis on punishment shifted firmly to reform and rehabilitation.

3 On the other hand, it was part of a trend in the declining use of the death penalty.

4 A far more significant turning point that led to change in the methods used to punish criminals was the building of new prisons, like Pentonville.

② Student's own response, but a suggested answer would be:

One reason that the abolition of the death penalty for most crimes in 1965 was a turning point was it broke with a trend in relying on its use for the most serious crimes. In the 1800s, the Bloody Code listed 222 crimes, but this fell to 60 crimes by 1832 and its use continued to narrow to the most serious crimes. As a result, up until its abolition, the death penalty was viewed as an important deterrent to serious crime. Its abolition was a turning point because the trend towards deterrence for crimes such as murder was broken.

Unit 8

Page 72

① a B b A c C d C

② **Tick:** Technology provided tools to improve the detection of crime, but government support and community involvement were also important factors

Page 73

① **1765:** The number of crimes on the Bloody Code rises to 160.

1777: John Howard publishes *The State of Prisons in England and Wales*, helping to bring about prison reform.

1787: Transportation to Australia begins.

1810: The number of crimes on the Bloody Code reaches its highest point at 222.

1817: Elizabeth Fry sets up the Association for the Reformation of Female Prisoners at Newgate.

1832: The Death Act reduces the number of crimes carrying the death penalty to 60.

1842: Pentonville Prison is built, following the principles of the separate system.

1865: The Prisons Act ensures that prisoners live in harsh conditions and do hard labour.

1868: The government ends the use of transportation and public executions.

1877: The government takes over control of all prisons.

Page 74

② A g; B f; C e; D b; E d; F c; G a

③ **JH:** They campaigned to ensure prisoners were released when they finished their sentence; They visited gaolers to persuade them to improve prison conditions and practices.

RP: They reduced the number of capital offences by 100 in 1825; They passed a law to ensure that gaolers were paid, so they did not exploit prisoners.

EF: They visited gaolers to persuade them to improve prison conditions and practices. They led Bible classes and taught sewing at Newgate Prison. They tried to improve conditions at Newgate Prison.

④ Students should insert the words in this order: retribution; Bloody; execution; humanitarian; separate; hard; hard.

Page 75

① **Topic focus:** the effectiveness of policing

Timeframe: the 19th and 20th centuries

Judgement: technology was the most important factor

② and ③ Student's own response, but might include:

Individuals: The work of Robert Peel X

Institutions: The role of the government X

Science: Developments in forensic science X

Technology: Detection technology ✓

Technology: Technology that improved communication ✓

Attitudes in society: Increased public support for the police X

④ Student's own response, but you might include:

Communication technology: Technology improved the way in which police officers could communicate with one another.

Robert Peel: Robert Peel set up the first official police force.

The government: The government passed laws to help strengthen the police force.

Forensic science: Developments in forensic science, for example the use of DNA evidence, helped solve crimes.

Public support: Increased public support for the police improved community involvement in the detection of crime.

⑤ Student's own response.

Page 76

① Student's own response, but you might write: Was it the police decision to focus on crime prevention or technologies to detect crime that made policing more effective?

② and ③ Student's own response might include:

Point	It was **technology** that improved the detection of crime by the police.	It was developments in **forensic science** that improved the detection of crime by the police.
Evidence	The National Automatic Fingerprint Identification System and the National DNA database were set up in 1995.	The discovery of unique fingerprint patterns, blood types and DNA helped improve crime detection.

Explanation	The databases made it possible to use crime scene evidence to track down some criminals.	These developments allowed crime scene evidence to be analysed to connect a suspect with a crime.
Weight	+	

4. Student's own response, but you might suggest: Scientific development is only significant when it is put to use on a large scale.

Page 77

1. Student's own response, but you might add the following additional arguments:

   For: Technology enabled the police to get to crime scenes quickly.

   Against: The government helped to strengthen the police force.

2. Student's own response, but you might weight as follows:

   A: Technology improved the effectiveness of police in identifying criminals. +4

   B: Technology enabled the police to get to crime scenes quickly. +3

   C: Robert Peel set up the first official police force. –2

   D: The government helped to strengthen the police force. –5

3. Student's own response, but you might write:

   B +3 Technology affected a lot of victims of crime, because they could communicate with, and be met by, police at a faster rate. However, it was still not effective enough to frequently catch criminals while still committing their crime.

   C: –2 Peel's work had an impact throughout the timeframe, but relied on new government legislation to develop it into an effective police force.

   D: –5 The government had a huge impact, creating police forces across the country, supporting the specialisation of police and funding new technologies and developments.

Page 78

1. Suggested annotations are as follows:

   Features of a strong conclusion

   Use of criteria to support judgements

   Direct comparison of other factors

   References to the argument for and against

   Strong student response: The most important factor in changing approaches to policing was the support from the government in setting up police forces, such as the Metropolitan Police, because without their legislation and funding, the first police force could not have been set up and used as a template for other police forces. Their support was more important than new technology, because even though the development of speed cameras and CCTV helped the police to catch criminals, the police still needed government funding, as well as legal support for the deployment of these technologies, to use them. However, the police could only change their approach if they had the means to do so, which is why developments in computing technology were important, as they enabled the police to catch criminals more efficiently and more often. They also relied on public support, through programmes like Neighbourhood Watch, to improve the effectiveness of their focus on the prevention of crime. Even so, without government support, changing the roles of the police and supporting their work, policing would not have changed as much, because the government provided the basis for later changes and the funding to make them possible.

   Features of a weak conclusion

   Unsupported assertion: a judgement without criteria to support it

   Repetition of points from the essay

   The use of new evidence

   Weak student response: The government was the most important reason, because they were important to changing what the police did. However, there were other reasons, like advances in technology and changes in public attitudes. For example, mass video surveillance allowed the police to focus on the detection of terrorist activities. This was created by inventors and scientists, who were also important.

Page 79

1 and 3 Student's own response, but you might include:

Point 1: The growth in humanitarianism led to a decline in the Bloody Code and transportations, resulting in greater use of prisons. (+5)

Point 2: The desire to reform criminals increased the use of the separate system. (+3)

Point 3: The work of individual reformers led to changes in approach. (–3)

Point 4: The increased role of central government in punishment led to changes in prisons. (–4)

2. Referring to the suggestions above, you might suggest that points 1 and 4 conflict. Point 1 made a bigger contribution than 4, because without the desire for change, the central government would have no reason to legislate to bring it about.

3. Student's own response.

4. Student's own response, but an appropriate answer might be:

   Attitudes in society were the main reason why approaches to punishment changed, because these drove reformers such as Robert Peel and Elizabeth Fry to make changes. Attitudes also encouraged the government to make large-scale changes, centralising prisons and introducing ideas like the separate system and hard labour. However, actual change only occurred because reformers such as John Howard highlighted the need for change, encouraging gaolers to change their practices. Nevertheless, without changing attitudes to ensure the government and gaolers were receptive to new approaches, little would have changed.

Notes